If one is married, one's wife must live somewhere.

PAGE 1.

A LITTLE SHIP

By TAFFRAIL

AUTHOR OF PINCHER MARTIN. O.D.
THE SUB ETC.

ILLUSTRATIONS BY H.R.J.

W & R CHAMBERS LIMITED
LONDON & EDINBURGH

Edinburgh:
Printed by W. & R. Chambers, Limited.

First Printed, Dec. 1918.
Reprinted,   Dec. 1918.

TO

THE LITTLE SHIP

AND

ALL WHO SERVED IN HER

CONTENTS.

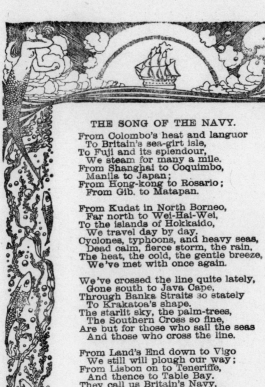

THE SONG OF THE NAVY.

From Colombo's heat and languor
  To Britain's sea-girt isle,
To Fuji and its splendour,
  We steam for many a mile.
From Shanghai to Coquimbo,
  Manila to Japan;
From Hong-kong to Rosario;
  From Gib. to Matapan.

From Kudat in North Borneo,
  Far north to Wei-Hai-Wei,
To the islands of Hokkaido,
  We travel day by day.
Cyclones, typhoons, and heavy seas,
  Dead calm, fierce storm, the rain,
The heat, the cold, the gentle breeze,
  We've met with once again.

We've crossed the line quite lately,
  Gone south to Java Cape,
Through Banka Straits so stately
  To Krakatoa's shape.
The starlit sky, the palm-trees,
  The Southern Cross so fine,
Are but for those who sail the seas
  And those who cross the line.

From Land's End down to Vigo
  We still will plough our way;
From Lisbon on to Teneriffe,
  And thence to Table Bay.
They call us Britain's Navy,
  And for ages long since past
No ocean but has known us,
  No sea we have not crossed.

From Cape Farewell down to the Horn,
  Rio to Simon's Bay,
'Cross Cancer and 'cross Capricorn,
  We still roam day by day.
Bad weather cannot stop us;
  Fogs, ice, or scorching sun;
Our march goes on for ever,
  Though we fall out one by one.
                'TAFFRAIL.'

CHINA, 1907.

A LITTLE SHIP.

CHAPTER I.

THE OLD SHIP AND THE NEW.

I.

I WAS working in the garden, hoeing the potato-patch, to be precise. Certainly, you may say that a naval officer has no right to have a house and a small strip of garden in war-time. He should be at sea, confounding the King's and his own enemies; but, as luck would have it, my ship had come in from sea that very morning. Moreover, it was the twenty-third of the month, and of those three-and-twenty days in the merry month of May we had spent no fewer than seventeen and three-quarters gallivanting about the North Sea on our lawful business. I forget how many miles we had steamed.

Also, if one is married, one's wife must live somewhere, and, as it happened, we had taken this particular house a full six months before the Kaiser set Europe ablaze from end to end. It was not until some time later, however, that we converted half the minute lawn at the back of the establishment into a potato-patch. It was some business, too, and the first year we got no potatoes larger than walnuts.

The family life of naval officers is always peculiar. We, the husbands, spent most of our time at sea, only getting ashore for a few hours in the afternoons when there was nothing doing. But activity and relaxation alternated with such frequency. At five o'clock in the morning one might actively be confounding the unspeakable Boche on the high seas ; while twelve hours later, arrayed in flannels, one disported one's self in mixed doubles on the tennis-courts. The Hun was always close. Indeed, one could even strafe him, or be strafed, at breakfast-time, and be sowing sweet-peas in one's garden by two in the afternoon. And long before Zeppelin or aeroplane raids were carried out on London, our wives, hanging out of their bedroom windows at all hours of the night, and in strict defiance of the warnings of the special constables, were wont to regard the sausage-shaped monsters floating in the sky and illuminated in the beams of the search-lights. Rumour even said that the wives living in one road, in necessarily *négligé* raiment, were wont to forgather in each other's houses for late suppers or early breakfasts, call them what you will, after these entertainments ceased.

So, as they badly wanted it, I was hoeing the potatoes, while Michael, our eight-year-old Irish terrier, who loves gardening, was sitting on his haunches with his tongue hanging out, superintending my labours. Dick, the

Sealyham, was absent from his place of duty at his master's side. He was investigating a neighbour's dust-bin.
I am still thinking of a satisfactory method of camouflaging dust-bins.

Then it was, at about half-past three, that I saw Parsons coming down the road in some haste, with his baggy-bottomed trousers flapping in the breeze. Parsons was my blue-jacket servant, and I knew from experience that his unexpected arrival in the middle of the afternoon signified something out of the ordinary.

'Well,' I asked, going to the gate to meet him, 'what is it? Raise steam?'

'No, sir. It's a signal,' said he, removing his cap and producing a folded paper from the lining thereof, the place where the sailor invariably places important documents for safe keeping. 'The sub-lootenant thought you'd like to have it at once, sir.'

He mopped his shining face, for the day was hot and he had walked fast.

The sub-lieutenant was wrong in his surmise, for I read the paper with my eyes starting out of my head, and feeling sick all over.

'You are appointed to *Triptolemus*,' it said

tersely. 'Your relief in present ship will be joining to-morrow, Thursday.'

It had come at last. I had half expected to leave for some months, for my time was up, and the ship, though people had come to gaze at her in admiration and envy in 1914, when she was yet considered rather a wonderful craft of a new type, was becoming elderly, and was leaving shortly for a new sphere of activity. Destroyers age rapidly in war-time, when they are turned out by the score. But I had served for two and a half years in her, had been in her, in fact, ever since she had come brand-new out of the builders' yard in '14, and hated the idea of turning her over, with her crew, to some one else. I looked upon her as my ship. We had grown up together, so to speak, until I knew, or thought I knew, her every whim and fancy, her every rivet and stanchion.

There was a dent in her side to remind me of the dark and blustery night when she became contrary, and no artifice of mine would induce her to answer her helm, and I nudged her rather hard into an oiler. There was a wrinkle in the stern plating where a blunt-nosed steam-trawler had butted into the poor old dear, and a piece of new plate on the forecastle and another on the ship's side where a descending 6-inch shell from a shore battery had driven its way through the mess-deck and overboard without exploding. If the fuse of that shell had been a little better I should not be writing this.

That particular projectile had been one of many others which nearly, but not quite, did for us. Three or four miles of hostile coast had sparkled with wicked-looking gun-flashes, while we, dodging all we knew how, had run the gauntlet with spray fountains darting out of the water all round us and the air full of a terrifying, demoniacal screeching. Altogether it had been one of the most exciting days in our lives, and on the mess-deck, to commemorate the occasion, attached to the beam overhead at the spot where the shell came through, was a mahogany strip bearing an inscription in brass letters. 'Lest we forget our Easter Monday, 1916,' it read; though it was far too merry a Bank Holiday for any of us to be likely to banish it from our memories.

Yes; I loved that ship and everything to do with her. I was fond of her officers and men, for most of us had served together in fair weather and foul, in good times and in bad, for thirty months—thirty months of war. And war, with all its trials and vicissitudes, welds a ship together in no uncertain manner. Ship's company, officers, and vessel learn to work together in a way that years of peace-time training can never accomplish; and living constantly on board our little craft made us know each other's virtues and accomplishments, faults and failings, ways and tricks, to a nicety. We had all been through the mill together. We had learnt, in the great majority of cases, through bitter experience.

Altogether we fancied that our ship was THE ship of the whole destroyer navy. I don't say that she was any better than many others ; merely that we thought so. After all, she was OUR ship, and we took an over-whelming pride in her ; and that, if you come to think of it, is the life and soul of the service.

And the flotilla, too, the force to which we were all so proud to belong—it was a bitter wrench to have to leave it, to cast aside the friends and associations of thirty months, and to have to start afresh elsewhere. It felt like going to a new school.

And who on earth was Triptolemus, any-way ? I did not discover until afterwards that he was the son of Oceanus and Terra, a great favourite of the goddess Ceres, who cured him of a dangerous illness in his early youth, and subsequently taught him agricul-ture. Afterwards, in Ceres's chariot drawn by dragons, he carried seed-corn to all the inhabitants of the earth, and imparted to them the knowledge given to him by the goddess.

No ; Mr Triptolemus, a fearful mouthful which the sailors would never be able to pronounce, left me rather cold. I much pre-ferred my old ship, which was named after a bygone admiral, an officer who had led the fleet into action at Copenhagen, and in reference to whom the immortal Nelson him-self, when asked to select a 'captain of the fleet,' or master-navigator on his staff, said, 'I will have —— or none'

We had heard of this saying from the present-day relatives of the gallant old warrior, whose picture hung in our wardroom; and from the very date of commissioning '—— or none' had been our proud motto. We had it exhibited on deck in brass letters on a scroll for everybody to see and to admire, and beneath it was a brass plate giving an abbreviated account of our namesake's career.

So I was very sad when I thought of what the old ship meant to me.

'You'd better go back to the ship and start packing my gear,' I told Parsons glumly.

He saluted and went off; while I, sick at heart and utterly miserable, went into the house to break the evil news to the sharer of my woes and joys.

'What is the name of the new destroyer?' she asked.

'*Triptolemus*,' I said very distinctly.

'Never heard of him,' she said. 'But I suppose it means giving up the house?'

'I'm afraid so. I know she isn't coming here.'

She fingered a china ornament on the mantelpiece, and looked very troubled, for the house was the same to her as the ship was to me. We had been married for eight years, during most of which we had followed a sort of nomad existence in rooms—rooms good, bad, and strangely indifferent. This was the first house of our own we had ever lived in.

I did my best to console her.

'Well,' she said at last, smiling in spite of her feelings, 'I suppose it can't be helped; but I shall simply hate giving up all this—simply hate it! I sha'n't see anything of you; and even if I do, I suppose it will mean living in dirty, smutty rooms again!'

'It's the fortune of war, poor old girl! I can't help it. I must go where they send me.'

And so, very sadly, we went together into the garden and talked it over, while I continued to hoe the potatoes. I felt I absolutely must do something to divert my thoughts, and for the time I was far too overcome to recollect that somebody else would benefit by my labours, that some one I had never seen might eat the potatoes we had taken such infinite care and trouble in planting.

And at that instant Dick, with a succulent chicken-leg in his mouth, and a sheepish expression on his face, came trotting down the garden-path. Now, chicken-bones out of other people's dust-bins are not good for little dogs. Chicken-bones are not good for them in any circumstances, since they are apt to splinter. So there was trouble in the camp, and the culprit, dropping his booty, yelped twice and fled like a streak of triple-greased lightning. Michael, with an expression on his face which said, 'Well, I'm a jolly good dog, anyhow. You never catch me dust-binning,' looked on and smiled. No; we had never caught him at dust-bins, but he sometimes developed an unholy penchant for rolling on dead sea-gulls.

II.

By the next evening, having turned over my orders, books, papers, and documents to my relief, and having said good-bye to officers and men, I was a gentleman at large. But not for very long, for forty-eight hours later my wife and myself were in the train on our way to the northern port where the *Triptolemus* was being built. It would be ten days before I finally took the ship over from the contractors and  sallied forth on the high seas; and ten days with one's wife in war-time, even in a strange hotel, are too good to be missed.

And one fine morning I found myself standing on a wooden jetty in a busy ship-building yard gazing at my new ship. Ugly as her name was, I must confess that I liked the look of her, and, from what they told me, she promised to be a good three knots faster than the old vessel. So I went on board, and delved into every hole and corner—the bridge, mess-decks, wardroom, cabins, engine-room; everywhere, in fact, where I possibly could go without upsetting the dozens of workmen who swarmed on board with their tools and pots of paint. And, lo! I began to take an interest in the ship, for I found her good. The 'chief,' otherwise the engineer officer, whom I had met before, had joined several months previously to superintend the preliminary trials and the placing on board of the various engines, machines, and fittings pertaining to his special department — boilers, turbines, pumps, air-compressors, steering-engine, and a hundred and one other gilguys, whose names alone were familiar to me. The gunner (T) had also made his appearance some weeks before, and what with his torpedoes and electrical apparatus, which seemed to arrive piecemeal and daily in wooden crates and cases, some the size of pantechnicon vans, and others barely larger than cigar-boxes, he was a very busy man.

The 'advance party,' a few ratings of the deck and engine-room departments, had come north with him from their depot, and were billeted in quarters outside the yard. In fact, the first thing I had to listen to was a bitter complaint as to the inferiority of the break-fasts supplied to them. The matter was soon rectified, but surely it takes a bluejacket to grumble at boiled haddock and poached eggs for the morning meal.

The rest of the crew would join just before the final trials, and they, from what I could see of it, would have their work cut out to get the ship ready by her proper date; for not very far away was a large shed filled to over-flowing with mountains of stores in bales, crates, drums, and packing-cases, which some-

how had to be stored on board. Everything
was there, from spare sparking-plugs for the
motor-boat to candles, from screw-drivers to
sealing-wax. And a little farther away, in a
special building, padlocked, sealed, and guarded
by a private of the Royal Defence Corps
wearing the '82 Egyptian ribbons, were the
shell and cartridges for the guns, the T.N.T.
filled warheads for the torpedoes, and other
highly dangerous and explosive contrivances
with which we hoped presently to achieve the
discomfiture of Brother Boche.

My first interview with the shipyard
manager, Mr Matthew, to whose office I
presently went to make my number, was
rather unexpected, to say the least of it. I
found myself in the presence of a thick-set,
sturdy little man, with bristling iron-gray hair,
keen gray eyes, and a ferocious expression.
Evidently he knew destroyer officers of old
—he should have, seeing that his firm turned
out a destroyer every six or eight weeks—and
regarded them as villains of the most lurid
dye, who wished to run away, or persuade him
into parting, with all the paint and enamel
in his perishing old shipyard. Indeed, after
my introduction by 'the chief, my polite
'Good-morning!' and a perfunctory handshake,
he stood there regarding me in a fierce and
stony silence, with his eyebrows bristling like
a nail-brush. Not that he alarmed me. On
the contrary, I was merely amused, and began
to wonder what had bitten him, or if this was
his usual behaviour.

Then he burst forth. 'Good-morning, commander! I'm glad to meet you, and before long I hope to speed the parting guest!'

I must confess that he didn't look pleased to see me; but his remark about speeding the parting guest struck me as rather inhospitable.

'There is one thing I want you to understand,' he went on in a roar like a bull of Bashan, 'and that is'—he paused, looking at me to see how I was taking him, and then wagged an admonitory finger in my face and leant forward as if he were telling me something highly confidential—'that is, that not one drop of paint, not one speck of enamel, not one pint of varnish, beyond the bare Admiralty allowance, will I put on board your ship!' And with this final remark he thumped his fist on the desk until the inkpot nearly capsized. 'That's flat, isn't it?' he bellowed.

'Good heavens!' I thought to myself; 'verily, the man must be mad!'

'I am not aware that I have asked for enamel or varnish,' I said in my most conciliatory manner.

'No; but you will sooner or later!' he almost shouted, wagging that forefinger of his in front of my nose. 'You're all tarred with the same brush! I know you!'

I laughed.

'Now we understand each other,' he went on more gently. 'I hope I shall see you at lunch at one-thirty. He,' indicating the chief, 'will show you where we have it. Let me see,' he added innocently, screwing up one eye. 'How long is it you've been with us?'

'About five months,' the chief told him.

'And five months too long!' snapped the most remarkable Mr Matthew, with the sweetest of smiles. 'I sha'n't be at all sorry to see the last of you. Speed the parting guest!'

But the heart of Mr Matthew, for all his abrupt manner, was very much in the right place; while the shipyard over which he held sway was one of the most efficient I have ever known. His firm have built men-o'-war of all classes for many long years, and if they stipulated to deliver a ship at such and such a time, she was completed to the very day, hour, and minute agreed upon; while such a thing as a break-down on the trials was practically unheard of. Their ships are good ships, and the *Triptolemus*, as we soon discovered, was very good.

The daily lunch with the firm's bigwigs was quite an amusing function. All the naval officers attended, and Mr Matthew kept us very much alive, particularly when he regaled us with stories of the Dumtavish Salmon Club. Only Mr Matthew can tell you what the D.S.C.—Salmon Club, I mean, not Distinguished Service Cross—exists for. Personally, I don't think it has much to do with salmon, except in the mayonnaise. There were also friendly disputes with Mr Bunderson, the firm's secretary, in regard to certain of Mr Bunderson's adventures in London.

And Mr Matthew had a wonderful memory. He seemed to remember everything he had ever read, particularly the *Ingoldsby Legends* and *The Dead Drummer of Salisbury Plain*. Moreover, he was a man of habit. Every day at lunch he was provided with a large tumbler of soda-water, all of which, except about three inches, he drank with his food. At the close of the meal he was handed a wine-glass half-full of whisky, and this he diluted with half the remains of the soda from the tumbler. He then consumed half the contents of the wine-glass, and re-diluting the remains with the rest of the soda, disposed of that. But the remarkable thing about the ritual was that he never by any chance made a miscalculation. I watched him many times, but never once did I observe him fail to leave exactly the right amount of soda in the large tumbler.

And that trivial habit, absurd though it may sound, was indicative of more important things. The accuracy with which it was carried out day after day was typical of the spirit of orderliness, routine, and efficiency which prevailed in the shipyard, and both the remarkable Mr Matthew and the establishment he represents have my sincere admiration. They turn out the best and the soundest of ships I have ever come across, if the *Triptolemus* is a fair sample of their handiwork. I say so advisedly, for a good few thousand miles of sea-water have passed under her bottom since the day we commissioned her. The shipyard well deserves its nickname of

'The Portsmouth Dockyard of the North.'
Indeed—— But what is the good of my enlarging on the subject? Nothing that I can

say will add to its reputation, nor could the
adamantine Mr Matthew ever be caused to
blush.

Speaking of shipyards, by the same token,
reminds me of something. Do you know
why, in all Government and private dockyards,
the hard billycock hat is the universal headgear in use by all the more important officials,
the inspectors, and the foremen? It is as
much the badge of their exalted office as are
the gaiters of a bishop, or the 'brass hat' in
either of the services.

Why do they wear this unbecoming and
inconvenient headgear? Why, to keep possible red-hot rivets descending from aloft from
impinging on their valuable skulls. One is
tempted to think that the heads of the actual
workmen must be very hard.

CHAPTER II.

COMMISSIONED.

I.

WE have now been in commission for some months. The time is 4.15 pip emma; the season, the early part of winter; and now, having finished tea, which meal, so far as I am concerned, consists of a piece of ship's biscuit and a cup of liquid of a rich burnt-sienna colour, the acidity of which would dissolve a tenpenny nail, I am at liberty to retire to my cabin to start this second chapter.

We have food at peculiar hours on board ship. Lunch is at twelve noon, and tea at half-past three; and the latter meal, from my point of view, is a fraud, a delusion, and a snare. The sub and the doctor, however, seem to enjoy it. They defy the Food Controller by eating hot buttered toast camouflaged with jam or potted meat, also slabs of solid-looking 'Scotch bun' sent for their delectation by one or other of their sisters or female cousins, who seem to think that they are half-starved. I, not having a sweet tooth, do not indulge in such gormandising.

The weather is pestilential, and through the open scuttle over my writing-table I can hear the shrill whistling of the wind, and the swish, slap, and gurgle of the seas as they go racing by. It is blowing hard; while ever since the early morning, when the needle of our aneroid started to go backwards with some rapidity, it has been snowing, raining, and sleeting at irregular intervals. The temperature on deck, as some one tritely observed, is enough to freeze the tail off a brass monkey. I am only too thankful that we are not at sea.

Every now and then I can feel the ship quiver and tremble as a particularly strong blast catches her and tautens out the cable which secures us to the buoy. We have an anchor watch set, and steam up for slow speed lest anything should carry away, and we should start sailing merrily down the harbour amongst our closely packed friends to leeward. I sincerely hope that nothing will part, for I, for one, do not fancy playing battledore and shuttlecock in a crowded anchorage in a gale of wind with the short winter afternoon drawing in.

I spent the afternoon in a folding-chair in front of a blazing stove. I started off by reading a book, until, very soon, my thoughts overcame me and the volume dropped with a crash. I let it lie, and continued to think. Then a heavy, sea-booted gentleman started to walk ponderously up and down, up and down, on the thin deck overhead, varying the monotony every now and then by a few steps of a double-shuffle to keep his feet warm. I have every sympathy for cold feet, but evidently the sailor on the roof did not realise that a destroyer is little better than a hollow steel drum, and that I, so to speak, am one of

L.S.   B

the cockroaches living inside that drum. At any rate, his peregrination sounded like the triumphal progress of an elephant battery and the Lord Mayor's Show all rolled into one; so I roused myself, went on deck, and asked the cause of my affliction, with what politeness I could muster, to continue his antics farther afield.

Next, Dick, the Sealyham, who had made a very hearty lunch, and has the peculiar but doubtful accomplishment of being able to snore in several different keys, took up the tale. He lay asleep, spread out at full length on the carpet cheek by jowl with the stove, and started his dreams by fighting whole battalions of imaginary cats, in the process of which he indulged in volleys of muffled yelps and other inarticulate canine abuse. I repressed him with the toe of my boot, whereupon he opened one sleepy eye, winked at me dreamily, fetched a deep sigh, and rolled over on his back with an ecstatic expression, and his four absurd crooked little legs pointing straight to the heavens. For exactly two minutes he behaved as all good little dogs should, then broke out into a perfect pæan of triumph, punctuated by pig-like grunts and snorts, and an occasional shrill whistling, like steam escaping from a locomotive.

Really, for his size, Dick provides me with the most astounding orchestra I have ever listened to. He is far and away better than any gramophone. His tunes are so utterly unexpected, and he never by any chance conducts the same symphony twice running. However, I could stand no more of him, so put him on deck to get a breath of fresh air ; and the next thing I heard was the scuttering of claws as he and Ginger, our yellow cat, indulged in a wild marathon round and round the upper deck. There is no peace in this wicked world.

Dick, by the same token, is on board for punishment. He is in disgrace, for a few days ago he cost me a pretty penny by slaughtering six young turkeys and three hens, not to speak of pulling the tail-feathers out of a Plymouth Rock old enough to be his grandmamma. If I were to believe the infuriated owner of those misguided hens, they all laid eggs, in season and out of season, and were, with the turkeys, prize birds of the most recherché description. Positively, I couldn't get a word in edgeways.

No wonder a European war costs something like seven millions sterling per diem. Dick's little battle cost me seventeen shillings and sixpence, and I'll guarantee it didn't last longer than forty-five seconds. That, if you care to indulge in abstruse calculations, works out at the magnificent sum of six hundred and thirteen thousand two hundred pounds per annum.

Dick is evidently a war lord by nature—a war lord of the fiercest description.

We have been five months in commission to-day, which reminds me of the heading of this chapter, and that I have yet to learn to stick to the point.

II.

Generally speaking, a ship is said to be 'out
of commission,' or 'paid off,' when she is laid
up for a lengthy refit and her officers and men
are not living on board. But there is room
for misapprehension in the matter. Take,
for instance, the case of Nelson's famous
Victory, which still does duty as the flagship
of the Commander-in-Chief at Portsmouth.
If you turned her up in the Navy List, the
unabridged edition of which is inaccessible to
the general public during war, you would find
under her name a list of nearly four hundred
officers, including the Commander-in-Chief
himself. Moreover, to hazard a wild guess,
at least ten thousand men must wear the
'H.M.S. *Victory*' cap-ribbon.

These officers and men all belong to the
various shore establishments at Portsmouth—
the Royal Naval Barracks, the Signal School,
and so forth; while the gallant old three-
decker herself, though she still flies an
admiral's flag and answers all salutes, is
manned by a 'care and maintenance party'
of barely more than twenty men. Courts-
martial are also held on board her in the cabin
once occupied by the immortal Nelson, for,
though a court-martial room was once erected
in some naval barracks, I believe it to be a
fact that no naval trial could legally be held
ashore until this war.

Take the *President*, again, the names of
whose officers fill thirty-one closely printed

columns in the Navy List, and whose number must run into thousands. I doubt if many of them have ever set foot on board the 1140-ton *President* (late *Buzzard*, late sloop), moored off the Temple Pier, London, the vessel to which, by legal fiction, they all belong. They are employed in the various departments and divisions of the Admiralty, and on miscellaneous and special services all over the United Kingdom. Even the officer who has the title of 'Inspector of Coals' in Scotland nominally belongs to the *President*.

The act whereby a man-of-war is commissioned, the ritual which transforms her from a hulk into a fighting-vessel, is simplicity itself. It consists merely in hoisting the White Ensign and the narrow, whip-like pendant, even the ancient formality of the commanding officer reading his commission to the assembled ship's company having fallen into desuetude. The process of commissioning, however, the preparation involved in making a ship into an efficient fighting machine, is quite a different matter. It necessitates a deal of careful organisation and hard work; while, let it be said, no vessel is thoroughly herself until she has been several months in commission, and her crew have had time to shake down and have learnt to work together. But of commissioning the *Triptolemus*, more anon.

Apropos of the pendant, however, the badge of every commissioned man-of-war which does not fly the flag of an admiral or the broad pendant of a commodore. It is hardly necessary to recapitulate the story of the celebrated Admiral Martin Van Tromp, who, during the Dutch wars of the mid-seventeenth century, proved such a sharp thorn in the side of us British. Indeed, it was on 30th November 1652 that the Dutchman, with a fleet of eighty ships and three hundred merchantmen, encountered Blake in the Strait of Dover and worsted him. It was after his victory that Van Tromp is said to have sailed on up the North Sea with a broom at his mast-head, as a sign that he had swept the British from the face of the sea.

The Dutch admiral is reported to have hoisted the broom at his mast-head as a sign of contempt for our fleet in much the same way as Von Capelle, Von Tirpitz, and certain other Teutonic naval gentlemen might possibly like to do in the present year of grace nineteen hundred and eighteen. But it must be admitted that in sixteen hundred and something we had a very difficult job in preventing the Dutch from doing what they pleased. Was it not in 1667 that a hostile squadron, under De Ruyter, sailed up the Medway to sink shipping, and to destroy dockyards and storehouses?

Blake, the British admiral—he was really a general, by the way, before he took to commanding fleets and winning battles afloat—is supposed to have retaliated to Van Tromp's insulting broom by hoisting a 'whip at the mast of his ship,' as a sign that he would presently lash the Dutchman into submission.

He carried out this threat; and it was from this whip, we are sometimes told, that the present-day man-of-war pendant, the narrow, white streamer with the red St George's cross next the mast, is supposed to have originated.

But it was not. The pendant came into use long before Blake's time. It started in the days of the Henrys, when seamen were mere nobodies; when there were no such things as regular men-of-war, and ordinary merchant-ships were hired or commandeered for use as fighting-vessels whenever the necessity arose. These requisitioned ships were commanded by military officers, gentlemen in armour, who, on embarking, transferred the single-tail pennons borne on their lances to the mast-heads of their ships. In larger vessels or squadrons, moreover, the commanders might be knights or knights banneret, who flew their swallow-tailed and square banners when they risked themselves afloat. Going to sea in those days was always something of an adventure, especially if one fell overboard in armour; but these emblems of command and authority have been handed down to posterity in the commodores' broad pendants and the admirals' rectangular flags of the present day.

III.

Some time before the war I was appointed as the 'executive officer' of a small cruiser with a complement of about three hundred officers and men. In other words, I was the senior officer of the deck department next to the captain himself, and, as such, was responsible to him, not only for the efficiency, cleanliness, and organisation of the vessel herself, but also for the well-being and comfort of every soul on board. If the staff-surgeon required his cabin painted, for instance, he came to me. So did the lieutenant (N.) when the roof of his domicile leaked on to his bunk. So did the paymaster when he thought he had discovered a plague of rats in one of his storerooms, and the ship's cook when his galley was invaded by a pest of cockroaches.

In fact, I was a sort of managing director of a species of Army and Navy Stores, Unlimited, whose employees lived, ate, slept, and worked on the premises. We had even our gentlemen's outfitting, household goods, ironmongery, stationery, grocery, and fancy-goods departments, and a good many others besides. The Army and Navy Stores, however, is blessed by the fact that it does not have to cruise around the country-side at twenty-three knots or less; while it does not have to organise itself for active strife against the establishments of Messrs Harrods, Whitely, or Selfridge. The building can never come into violent collision with St Paul's Cathedral, the Houses of Parliament, or the British Museum on a dark and foggy night; nor does it indulge in such antics as letting go anchors from the top-storey windows if it comes on to blow a gale of wind. We had to consider all these things, and a good many more.

I had always known that commissioning a ship involved no small amount of labour, but how hard the work actually was I never thoroughly realised until I did the job myself. One requires the temper of an angel and the judgment of a Solomon; and remember that my ship was a light cruiser, not a battleship or battle-cruiser manned by close on a thousand officers and men.

My first care was to go and look at the ship herself. She was by no means new to start with, and before I joined her she had been out of commission for the purpose of being re-armed with more modern and larger guns. It was a streaming wet day in a particularly dismal January when I first came across her, forlorn and neglected, in a dry-dock in Portsmouth dockyard. I went on board, and, after my first glance, felt inclined to fall in with the mood of the weather by bursting into bitter tears.

Talk of the Augean stables and the labours of Hercules! His job was nothing to what it seemed I should have to do.

Eight months before, if my memory is not at fault, that ship had been paid off at Devonport. She had been left in the dockyard there for a month or two, with not a soul to care for her, and was then refitted. After this she was suffered once more to relapse into a state of torpitude for another three months, then suddenly had a 'navigating party' thrust on board her. They steamed her to Queenstown in Ireland, and there handed her over to the authorities to have the new guns placed on board; after which, another navigating party steamed her to Portsmouth. Then, once more, she was deserted by everybody except the dockyard police.

Not a scrubber, a broom, or a scraper seemed to have touched her since she had been paid off eight months before. She had been anointed with paint from time to time to make her look pretty outside; while, in the intervals of visiting various dockyards and carrying out steam trials, she had embarked copious supplies of coal. As a consequence, and since there was nobody who really took an interest in her, the dockyard maties * had slapped on the service gray paint over coaldust and dirt alike, so that in places on her upper works which I tested with the point of a penknife for experimental purposes, there was a coating a third of an inch thick, without exaggeration. The paint on her side, moreover, which was streaked with red rust until the poor old thing looked like a zebra, was just as bad, and for the first six months of the commission we always had a party of ten men slung on stages chipping away for dear life. Before this time I had no idea of the weight of dry paint, but afterwards I had. I once collected over three pounds of it from a square yard of surface.

In places her wooden upper deck was half-an-inch thick in a hideous layer of the inevitable paint, dockyard mud, oil, the marine

* Dockyard maties—that is, workmen.

glue used for caulking the seams, and other unrecognisable ingredients. Walking on it, in fact, felt like being upon an asphalt pavement on a hot day in July. I noticed a piece of protruding spun-yarn, and pulled at the end of it. It yielded with some reluctance, and, walking forward, I disengaged a full fathom from the viscous, glue-like compound in which it was embedded. No mere scrubbing or holystoning would ever remove that terrible grime. For weeks after we commissioned, our malefactors, those unhappy mortals sentenced to extra work for their various misdemeanours, spent their leisure moments in chopping the filth from that deck with sharp scrapers.

On the mess-decks and down below in the various flats and compartments things were equally bad. Paint seemed to have been slapped on anyhow, candle-grease was spattered all over the woodwork, and a litter of rope-yarn, wastepaper, dust, wood-shavings, and empty tins, the relics of I know not what, were in every hole and corner.

The day I first set foot on board that ship, the day I received my appointment to her, was a Thursday, and on the next Tuesday as ever was, at nine o'clock in the morning, the crew were due to arrive by train from Chatham, and she was to commission. I was horrified at the prospect. The ship was in a terrible condition, and I hadn't even got a list giving the names, ratings, and qualifications of the men who were to form the ship's company. I hadn't even got the master-at-arms to assist me in writing up the watch bill, or to make out the commissioning cards, the printed tickets given to each man on joining, telling him what division he is to belong to, the number and position of his mess, where to stow his bag and hammock, and his stations for fire, collision, and in action.

My first task was to send a peremptory telegram to Chatham demanding the necessary nominal list of men and the immediate presence of the master-at-arms detailed for the ship. My second was a pilgrimage to the naval barracks, where, after some palaver, I eventually succeeded in borrowing a party of thirty newly joined stokers, all the men they could spare, to get the ship fairly presentable. They were doing me a favour in letting me have them; but they were not much help. They arrived on board at 8.30 on the Friday morning, and worked till 11.15, at which time they departed to the barracks for their dinner. They reappeared at 1.45, and worked till 3.15; while on Saturday, Sunday, and Monday they did not arrive at all. I say they 'worked,' but in reality, as I was far too busy to stand over them with a lethal weapon, they regarded their outing as a very pleasant little holiday. They spent most of the time smoking surreptitious cigarettes in out-of-the-way corners, and in wandering aimlessly round the ship looking for brooms, scrubbers, buckets, scrapers, soap, and cloths which I had placed ready to hand under their very noses. And, not content with this, they added insult to

injury by purloining most of the said utensils
when they finally left the ship.

At noon on the Friday the list giving the
names of the men arrived by express letter,
but still no master-at-arms. There was
nothing for it but to enlist the services of my
wife, and between us we worked from chilly
dawn till dewy eve making out the watch,
station, and quarter bills, and in drafting
and arranging the necessary routines, orders,
messes, sleeping-billets, and fifty and one
other matters which must be seen into before
the men arrive on board. We even had to
arrange for coal to be placed on board for the
galley, and for the coppers to be cleaned out
and filled with fresh water.
We managed it somehow,
living on hot coffee and
sandwiches in our lodgings
while we did it, but never
have we had a more ex-
hausting task.

At last, late on Satur-
day afternoon, the errant
master-at-arms made his
appearance. He, it would
appear, had been having
his teeth out, and imparted
the distressing information
that he still felt 'mortal
queer and not up to much.' His face certainly
did look rather distended. Moreover, to add
to the complications, he brought another
nominal list with him, and it did not tally

with the one we already had. Then it was
that I nearly burst into tears. We went to a
music-hall that night to drown our sorrows in
Mr George Robey—my wife and I, I mean;
not the master-at-arms and myself.

And on the Tuesday we got the old ship
commissioned, an astounding fact at which I
never ceased to marvel. It was no fault of
mine. By some merciful dispensation of
Providence, the things that really mattered
seemed to go off without any tangible hitch,
though it is true that while we were embarking ammunition a day or two later we had
the misfortune to drop a box of 4-inch lyddite
shell in the entrance to one of the dockyard
basins. The occurrence brought visions of
courts of inquiry to the officer responsible
for the incident, and occasioned some slight
flutter in certain official dovecotes. The next
heavy-draught battleship which came along
at low-water would certainly sit gently on
that box and blow herself sky-high, they
wisely observed. It was quite useless for us
to shake our heads, and to reply that the caps
were on the fuses of the shell and the safety-
pins in, and that we felt doubtful whether the
disaster they contemplated were possible even
if half-a-dozen Dreadnoughts played football
with the wretched box. They simply wouldn't
believe us. Nothing could persuade them
that the whole dockyard was not about to be
blown to smithereens; so nobody was really
sorry when, after six hours' search, a diver
recovered the booty.

After a week in commission we started to settle down, and things began to get into running order. In a month the routine and general work of the ship was becoming more or less cut and dried; while in three months officers and men thoroughly understood each other, affairs ran as smoothly as clockwork, and I had little to do except to exercise a general supervision. Not that I was idle. The executive officer of a ship, however small, can never be idle. I merely allowed the actual routine-work to become decentralised, and turned my attention to other and more important subjects.

But we never got the ship to look really clean. She had been so badly treated that her paint-work could never assume that glossy smoothness which so smartens a vessel, while teak-decks were so permeated and stained with grime that no amount of scraping, holystoning, and scrubbing with sand could ever bring them to that state of snowy whiteness which we so desired. She was clean, however, in that she was not actually dirty.

Five months after we commissioned, an admiral came on board to inspect us officially.

'The ship is in every way efficient as a man-of-war,' he wrote in his report; 'but she is not so clean as other vessels of her class which I have recently inspected.'

I foamed at the mouth. The other vessels to which the gilded potentate referred had not lain idle for eight mortal months, and if he could only have seen our ship on that dismal January day in Portsmouth dockyard when I first clapped eyes upon her, he might perhaps have modified his opinion.

But the captain, though he showed me the report with rather a glum expression, did not really mind. He knew as well as I did how we had been handicapped, and when I burst forth in disapproval, he was inclined to be sympathetic. After all, we weren't a yacht. We were a man-of-war, and in a fighting-vessel snowy cleanliness, speckless decks, and shining paint-work do not always work hand-in-hand with efficiency.

We were efficient—the admiral had said so —and that is all we really cared about.

I have said something of my experiences in a light cruiser, not because they were any way unusual, but merely to show that commissioning a new ship, like moving into a new house, may be an event which one cannot readily forget.

When we commissioned the *Triptolemus* we were beset by very few pitfalls. For one thing, our ship's company consisted of less than a hundred all told; while the ship, being brand-new, was as clean and as smart as a new pin. The men, of course, were strangers to the officers and to each other, but both the first lieutenant and myself had just come from another destroyer, of which the *Triptolemus* was a newer edition, in which we had served together for over two years. So two of us, at any rate, knew each other's ideas and habits, understood what to keep a watchful eye upon, and how to repress the comic proclivities of the inevitable funny man during working-hours. I have known the greater portion of a ship's company kept in a state of idle and hilarious excitement the whole of one fore-noon by the antics of one of their number with a piece of burnt cork. Our men could not afford to be idle. They had their work cut out to embark mountains of stores and ammunition, and to stow them on board in their various storerooms, magazines, and shell-rooms.

Before the ship was finally handed over to us she had to carry out her trials, and one sunny morning in June found us steaming down the river on our way towards the open sea. I don't know how many people there were on board. I omitted to count them, and merely remember having a vague recollection at the back of my mind that sixteen average men weighed approximately one ton. We carried several tons of extra, but not super-fluous, flesh, bone, blood, and muscle. The ship was crammed to bursting with the firm's officials and workmen, Admiralty representa-tives and overseers, not to mention the officers and men who would presently form the ship's company. We were merely there as spectators to take over in the remote possibility of our meeting a German submarine. A pilot was in charge, while the contractors' men ran the engines and fired the boilers.

'Supposing she breaks down on trial?' I injudiciously asked one of the firm's repre-sentatives.

'My good sir,' he replied with a look of injured horror, 'have you not learnt that OUR ships never break down?'

I apologised meekly, for he was perfectly right. A destroyer built by that particular firm appears every six weeks with the utmost regularity, and in no case has one of their vessels failed to exceed her contract speed. Nothing ever goes wrong, and the cut-and-dried programme is carried out to the very day, hour, and minute.

'At a quarter to seven to-morrow morning a motor will be waiting outside the door of your hotel,' Mr Matthew had told me at lunch the day before. 'After picking you up, it will call for our friends here,' indicating the chief and the Admiralty hull overseer.

'I shall be there,' I said.

'You had better be,' said Mr Matthew dryly. 'The ship waits for nobody, mind, not even the Prime Minister of Great Britain or the Bishop of Bath and Wells!'

'Are we to be honoured with their august presence?' I queried.

Mr Matthew glowered at my frivolity. 'No!' he snapped, wagging that finger of his. 'But the ship sails at seven-thirty by my watch, *D.V.* or not. If you aren't on board by that time, she goes without you; and that's all about it!'

'And shall we have the pleasure of your company?'

'The answer is in the negative.'

'Coward!' I retorted with a sweet smile.

whereat Mr Bunderson laughed, and the apostolic one became rather annoyed. He always resented one's taking liberties with him.

And by 7.20 precisely we, the naval people, were all on board ; while a few minutes later Mr Matthew, watch in hand, appeared on the jetty abreast the ship. At 7.30, to the tick, he shut his chronometer with a snap, thrust it into his waistcoat-pocket, and waved his hand to the pilot. The men on the jetty started to haul the gangway ashore, when suddenly I heard excited voices under the bridge.

' Has any one seen Mr Elkington ? ' somebody was asking loudly. 'We can't leave without him !'

Who Mr Elkington was I hadn't a ghost of a notion. I had never even heard about him, though, from the commotion caused by his absence, he was evidently a person of importance who had something to do with our trials.

'Mr Elkington is missing,' they told Mr Matthew.

' Damn Mr Elkington !' retorted Mr Matthew, grinding his teeth.

And just at that moment the cause of all the commotion shot round a corner as if the devil were after him. He—Mr Elkington, not the devil—clutched a bag and an umbrella in one hand, and a bowler hat in the other. He came on gallantly, his overcoat flapping in the breeze behind him. He was in a desperate hurry.

Mr Matthew, with a face like a thunder-cloud, produced his watch, and eyed him ferociously.

'I hope I'm not late,' the new-comer apologised, arriving breathless on the jetty and scrambling on board. 'The train'——

'Damn the train!' snorted the manager. 'You're two minutes fifteen seconds late, and I won't listen to your excuses. If Admiralty officials aren't punctual, how can you expect the contractors to deliver ships up to time, eh?'

But Mr Elkington, bag and all, was far out of earshot. The trial was quite satis-factory, and the *Triptolemus* exceeded her contract speed by at least two knots. More-over, the firm did not intend their representa-tives or ourselves to go hungry. On the contrary, they evidently realised the invigo-rating quality of the Scottish sea-air; for the wardroom table was specially lengthened, and their catering staff had staggered on board with enormous hampers of provisions and cases of bottled beer. And we did not go hungry, either. The Food Controller—— But the Food Controller was not there, so what does it matter?

And three days later, after an official in-spection, we left the shipyard for good and all; while Mr Matthew, a number of lesser celebrities, and a crowd of workmen assembled on the jetty to see the last of their handiwork. We steamed down the river, carried out the final 'acceptance trial,' and then anchored in the estuary and forgathered in the wardroom to sign the necessary papers transferring the ship to the Admiralty.

'Well, here's luck to the *Triptolemus*,' said the firm's senior representative, finishing his whisky-and-soda, screwing the cap on his fountain-pen, and reaching for his hat. 'I think you'll find her a good ship, and I hope you'll bag a submarine within a week. Don't go blowing yourself up on a mine, though!'

'Not if I can help it,' I laughed. 'Here's fortune to the firm!'

We followed them on deck, and a few minutes later the last of the contractors' men were scrambling into the tug alongside.

'Come along! Hurry up, men!' a bowler-hatted potentate on the paddle-box exhorted them, watch in hand. 'We shall miss the train if we aren't careful!'

The little vessel sheered off with a tootle of her whistle, a grinding of her paddles, and a waving of hats and handkerchiefs.

'*Au revoir!*' we called out after her.

'Good-bye! Good luck!' floated back. 'Hope you'll have a good passage!'

Ten minutes later, with her paddles stirring up the water behind her and a volume of black smoke pouring from her thin funnel, she was fading away in the distance. She was in a hurry. The people on board her had their train to catch. She somehow reminded me of a hungry, anxious chicken darting home at feeding-time.

And before very long our capstan was

heaving round, and the cable was coming slowly home.

'Anchor's away, sir!' came the shout from the forecastle.

'Clear anchor, sir!' as the muddy hook came to the surface.

The engine-room reply-gongs clanged noisily. The ship, gathering speed, turned on her heel, and an hour later we were in the open, the coast was fading into a bluey-gray line astern, and we were steaming at twenty knots in the teeth of a short, snappy little sea and a rapidly freshening breeze.   We had left the flesh-pots and amenities of civilisation behind us; but I, for one, was glad to be away.

'Now she feels it,' laughed the first lieutenant, as the ship started to bob and curtsy, and dollops of spray came driving across the forecastle.   'This'll shake the insides out of some of our people who've never been in a destroyer before.'

It did, for on looking over the bridge-rail I saw a mournful, white-faced little party— well, offering their first tributes to Neptune. Poor fellows!   They had my sincere sympathy.   They were fearfully and wonderfully indisposed.

Yet another destroyer had been added to His Majesty's Navy.   Yet another few ordinary seamen (for hostilities only) were learning from bitter experience that life in a T.B.D. is not all beer and baggy trousers.

Yet another destroyer had been added to His Majesty's Navy.

CHAPTER III.

I.

I HAVE just had occasion to send a Christmas card to a very near relation of my wife's, who is at present living at, in, or near a place called Llwyngwryl!

I need scarcely mention whereabouts in Great Britain Llwyngwryl is. It is not my fault, moreover, if I have spelt it incorrectly, for I can find it in no gazetteer or atlas to which I have access. The spelling is my wife's, who knows, or says she knows, a very great deal about the spelling of such names.

But it occurs to me that I am glad that Llwyngwryl is not a very well-known place. If it were, it might occur to the Lords Commissioners of the Admiralty to christen a ship after it, and, for my many sins, to appoint me to her. Such an event would be beyond a joke. It would be a calamity for which not even a handsome present from the mayor and corporation could atone. Perhaps Llwyngwryl does not possess such potentates; but even if it does, and they made us a gift of a set of silver candelabra and a statuette of his worship for the wardroom table, together with electroplated shaving-sets—suitably inscribed, of course—for every single member of the ship's company, we should never quite get over it.

Even the simple name *Triptolemus* has its pitfalls for the unwary. About one strange bluejacket in every ten says it correctly, and to most of them it is *Trip-tô-lē-mus*. But H.M.S. *Llwyngwryl* would be far and away worse, and nobody cares to serve in a ship whose name he cannot even spell or pronounce, and which, on paper, seems strangely reminiscent of a gentleman suffering from hay fever, or my Irish terrier Michael, who lives ashore, resenting the arrival of the milkman.

But I feel rather perturbed about it, for the Royal Navy, with its innumerable auxiliary small craft for war purposes, has some very peculiar names nowadays. What about H.M.S.'s *Cheerio Lads*, *Daily Bread*, *Familiar Friend*, *Kipper*, *Our Girls Three*, and *Young Archie*, to mention a few of them?

But even in the days of the Spanish Armada a vessel called the *Bark Buggins* was one of the hired merchant vessels serving under the orders of Sir Francis Drake. The *Elizabeth Jonas* and the *Elizabeth Bonaventure* were 'Queen's ships,' or regular men-of-war of the same period. Both were named after Queen Elizabeth—the first, in 1559, 'in the remembrance of her own delivery from the fury of her enemies, from which she was no less providentially preserved than was the prophet Jonah in the belly of the whale;' and the second, in 1561, because the Queen hoped for good luck in the future.

But none of these names quite comes up to that given to a ship of the line by the French

revolutionary Government. They called her
Sans Culottes, or ' Without Knee-Breeches ' !
The shining lights of the revolutionary period
wore trousers, let us hope. Nether garments
reaching to the knee were only favoured by
the effete and hated aristocracy.

But in our little ship we have occasional
misunderstandings about the name, quite
apart from its pronunciation.

On the stem-piece, right in the eyes of the
ship, we carry a Chinese joss for good luck.
I don't really know of what he is the presiding
genius ; whether, indeed, he is a ' he ' or a ' she ; '
but our joss is a little carved wooden image
about seven inches high, sitting in an arm-
chair. He—for we, somehow, think of him as
a gentleman—has a yellow face, slanting eyes,
and rather a mottled complexion, due to wind
and spray. He is attired in a golden dressing-
gown or *peignoir*, picked out in scarlet and
blue, and receives a fresh coat of gorgeous
gold-leaf and enamel every time the ship refits.
He was originally picked up in Hong-Kong
harbour after the great typhoon of 1906, when
many junks were capsized and wrecked, with
great loss of life. The joss—for he has no
name—has been with me in every destroyer
in which I have served since.

But it was this little image which mystified
one of our newly joined ordinary seamen.
' My dear father,' he wrote to his interested
parent, ' I am now serving on a ship called
the *Triptolemus*. I am not quite certain
whether she is named after an Indian or a

Japanese god, but we have his likeness stuck up on our forecastle!'

I know of another Chinese joss who also became a naturalised British subject, and served his time in destroyers. He was a relic of the Boxer business of 1900; and when his owner subsequently went 'destroying,' Henry, as he was called, went with him, and was fixed to the mast-head of his new ship. He, too, received his coat of gold-leaf and paint every time his vessel went to a dockyard; though once, during coaling, when a wire whip parted and injured a man, Henry, whose fault it was said to be, was punished by being red-leaded for ten days. So even josses are subject to the Naval Discipline Act.

Another officer had a stuffed Antarctic penguin at his mast-head in his destroyer days. The bird, moth-eaten though it may have been, evidently brought good luck, for another ship and his own met several German destroyers on a dark night in the English Channel. Between them they . . . Well, I need hardly relate the story of the *Swift* and the *Broke;* but certainly that penguin is a happy fowl, for both the officers concerned are now captains, and a good many other things besides. Moral—stick to poultry.

Most ships have mascots of some sort, inanimate or otherwise, but I shall have something to say about them later. Other matters over which we can exercise our wits, however, are mottoes; and among others I may mention the time-honoured 'Fear God and

honour the King,' 'Nil desperandum,' and
' Dum spiro spero,' all very laudable sentiments
in their way ; and ' Play the game ' and ' Play
fair.'

There is also a great deal of ingenuity in
the designing of crests and boats' badges. If
one is in a ship called after some old-time
naval officer the matter is fairly simple, for
one can write to his descendants and obtain
permission to use the family crest. If the
ship is called after a classical hero, too,
something can generally be routed out of a
classical dictionary. Little thought is also
required when a vessel is named after an
animal or a bird, though I believe there was
once some slight heart-burning in the case of
two of the well-known ' L ' class destroyers,
the *Lark* and the *Laverock*. It certainly is
a little bit awkward if two ships are called
after the same species of bird ; and in the case
of these two, each stoutly maintained that
the design adopted as a crest by the other
resembled a trussed chicken.

Our badge, since our namesake was an
agricultural expert who distributed corn, is
naturally a wheat-sheaf.

But surely the strangest badge of all must
be that used by a ship named the *Offa*, which,
the first time I saw it, gave me furiously to
rack my brains. It was nothing more nor
less than a sprig of ordinary common or garden
holly such as one sees stuck in the top of the
Christmas pudding. Now Offa was an ancient
English king who died in A.D. 796, and laid

down the sound axiom for an island kingdom that 'he who would be secure on land must be supreme at sea,' but for the life of me I could discover no analogy between him or his doings and a sprig of holly. Then some one took pity upon me and explained. A sprig of holly = Christmas. Christmas = Noel. Offa = Offal with no 'l'!

What a brain!

II.

Sailors, as some person far wiser than myself once remarked, are peculiar animals, though I do not think that in these enlightened days one hears of more eccentricity in the navy than in any other walk of life. Certainly I have never met, or even heard of, any modern successor to the famous 'Mad Montague,' a very well-known naval character of the late eighteenth century.

He, as the captain of a frigate, once went ashore at Lisbon, became embroiled in a quarrel at a 'low tavern,' and returned on board in the course of the evening with a wonderfully good specimen of a black eye. The next day, unhappily, he had to call on the admiral, and unwilling to be unduly conspicuous on stepping out of his boat, solved the difficulty by ordering the crew of his six-oared gig to titivate their eyes with burnt cork. The men pulling the port oars blacked their left eyes, those at the starboard oars their right, and the coxswain both. History does not relate the remarks of the officer of

the watch in the flagship on the arrival of the
battered-looking boatload.

Captain Montague was also the officer who,
when his ship was at Portsmouth, once asked
permission from the Commander-in-Chief to
visit London. As it was war-time, and his
ship might be ordered to sea at any moment,
the request was refused, the admiral adding
the unguarded remark that the captain must
go no farther from his vessel 'than his gig
could carry him.'

But Montague, a most ingenious person in
his way, was not to be overcome by a trifle
of this kind. He simply hired a brewer's
dray, mounted his boat upon it, provisioned
her for three days, and, with himself sitting
in full dress in the stern-sheets, and his boat's
crew with their oars rigged out going through
the motions of rowing, suffered himself
solemnly to be drawn through the dockyard by a team of horses *en route* for the
Metropolis.

The excitement was intense. The dockyard
workmen and the crews of various ships ceased
their labours to enjoy the strange spectacle,
and presently, as discipline in those days
was notoriously lax, the equipage was being
followed by a cheering, hilarious mob. The
uproar reached the ears of the admiral, who,
realising that he had been 'had,' and knowing
full well that no more work would be done
in the place until the gladsome procession
was out of sight, sent a messenger after
Montague to inform him that he might pro-

ceed to London how and when he pleased,
which was precisely what Montague knew
would happen. But I tremble to think of
the results of such an escapade in nineteen
hundred and war-time.

In more modern days one has heard of the
naval officer who insisted on choosing and
buying all the clothes for his wife and children,
with the most comical results ; and also of the
peppery naval officer who, when he retired,
was cured of his tantrums by his wife. A
ham and an underdone or overdone fowl, at
any rate an unprepossessing fowl of some
kind, once appeared on his dinner-table.

'Look at the damned thing!' he shouted.
'It's only fit for the dust-heap!' and straight
away hurled the offending bird through the
dining-room window.

'Very well, dear,' said his intrepid wife
gently. 'This damned thing had better go
too!' and she hurled the ham after the chicken.

There was once a lieutenant who wrote an
official letter to the Admiralty asking to be
appointed to a ship with a roof on it. He
had seen a housed-in depot ship at some port
or other, and evidently fancied a 'cushy' job
in harbour. The Admiralty, however, did not
approve of sending young and very junior
officers to ships with roofs, nor did they wish
to encourage frivolous letters. So a week
later, with grim irony, they appointed our
friend to a certain vessel in the Persian Gulf.
She had no roof, but did carry double awnings
in the hot weather !

It was this same officer, I believe, who once
lost his walking-stick in the club at Malta.
He promptly wrote a notice and placed it
conspicuously on the notice-board : 'Will the
nobleman who has stolen my walking-stick
kindly return it at once ? '

The only noble members of the club,
two honorary members of Maltese extraction,
naturally protested at such aspersions on their
honesty, and the naval officer was summoned
before a committee meeting to explain himself. 'Oh,' said he, ' the rules of the club say
that only noblemen, officers, and gentlemen
can be members ; and as no officer or gentleman can have stolen my stick, it must have
been a nobleman ! '

Sailors may be peculiar animals, and certainly, if you had stood on Portsmouth Hard
some years ago, and had watched the antics of
some bluejackets just paid off from their ship
after three years in the East Indies, you
might have agreed. A party of about twenty
emerged from the main gates of the dockyard,
carrying their little blue bundles. They were
ripe for mischief after months of the shiny
East, and boarding the nearest tram, demanded
loudly and insistently to be taken to Portsmouth Town station *en route* for their respective homes. But the driver, busy with a
sausage-roll and a mug of coffee in the door-
way of an eating-house, shook his head, and
observed that the conveyance was not due to
start for at least five minutes. So the seamen, clambering on to the roof, stamped their

L.S.   D

feet and whiled away the time by singing at the pitch of their lusty voices, until the incoming tram appeared and drew up on the opposite set of rails with its top deck nearly touching theirs. It was then that some ingenious soul, in a sudden fit of devilment, suggested lashing the two vehicles together. No sooner said than done, and, stripping off their black-silk handkerchiefs, they tied the rails of the two cars to each other, and then sat down, chuckling in mischievous glee, to watch what happened. Presently the driver, with his mouth still full, emerged from his lair, looked guiltily at the clock, and clambered on to the foot-board. The conductor followed him.

'Ting, ting!' went the bell, and round went the starting-lever.

No result at all, for the tram, secured to its opposite number, absolutely refused to budge.

(Suppressed titters from the roof; while one gentleman, apoplectic with amusement, was thumped heartily on the back by his mates.)

'Bill,' came a shout, 'you 'aven't got that 'ere pole o' yourn on the over'ead wire!'

Bill, the conductor, protested loudly that everything at his end was in perfect order, and the driver gradually gave her more juice until the sparks started to fly.

'Bill,' came another howl, 'I can't move 'er!'

(Shrieks of derisive merriment from the roof.)

'Go on, 'Orace! 'Ave another go!' from the conductor.

Horace did as requested. Nothing at all happened.

(Scene of pandemonium on the roof.)

Next, after much mutual recrimination between bow and stern, the conductor and the driver together removed their outer garments and began to examine the underbody of the vehicle. For quite five minutes they grovelled in the road, presently to emerge breathless, dishevelled, and vituperant.

'I can't see nothing wrong with 'er,' opined the driver, mopping a shiny face.

'Better telephone to the de-pot for some one to come an' 'ave a look at the blame thing,' suggested Bill.

Horace agreed, and once more disappeared into the eating-house to use the telephone.

''Ere, young fella'!' suddenly demanded a smiling blue-clad warrior from the top storey. 'What time does this bloomin' ship o' yours get under way?'

'We can't move 'er,' retorted the conductor angrily. 'Don't go askin' stoopid questions.'

'Don't go gettin' dizzy, Harchibald dear!' laughed another seaman, with a bright-red face, leaning perilously over the edge. 'Me and my mates wants to know what time this perishin' tram is due to start. We 'ave a train to catch, and when we asks a civil question we don't want no back-chat—see!'

'I'll give yer back-chat! I tell yer we

can't start it, an' the driver's gorn to telephone to 'eadquarters. Ain't that good
enough?'

'Can't start it, pudden-face! Why, wot
d'you call yourselves? Look 'ere, my man,
if we misses our train me and my mates 'll
report you to the mayor and corporation wot
owns these trams. You'll be disrated for
incompetence; see if you ain't!'

'Oh, shut yer fat 'ead, carn't yer? It ain't
my fault!'

'Then who's bloomin' fault is it, I wants
to know? This 'll 'ave to be inquired into.
We carn't allow these 'ere goin's-on on the
Pompey trams!'

'Oh, shut up!'

'Look 'ere, ole son,' from a bluejacket.
'Shall I 'ave a go at 'er?'

'You don't know nothin' about drivin'
trams!'

'Ho, don't I bloomin' well? Will you let
me 'ave a try?'

'Oh, 'ave yer try if yer wants to; but you
won't be able to do nothin'!'

'Right you are, me boyo,' said the rubicund
sailor, with a twinkle in his eye. 'Cast 'er
off, lads!' in a hoarse whisper to his friends.

The lads, speechless with amusement, un-
lashed the handkerchiefs unseen by the
conductor, and the fat sailor, clambering
heavily down the steps, took his place on
the front platform.

'Now,' he said, gripping the handle in his
mighty paw, 'you says I knows nothin' at all

abart it. I just shoves 'er over like this '—
pushing the lever to its fullest extent—' an'
away we goes!'

And go they did, at about twenty knots,
with the men on the roof hanging on for grim
death and cheering themselves hoarse.

I can still see the expression of absolute
consternation on the face of the driver when,
emerging from the eating-house, he saw his
tram careering wildly down the road; while
Bill, having succeeded in boarding the rear
platform, agitatedly rang the bell to bring the
swaying vehicle to a standstill. Then the
driver, jamming his cap firmly on his head,
darted off in pursuit. He would never have
caught it; indeed, the tram would have been
derailed if it had gone round a curve at such
a speed, but the bluejacket driver wisely
stopped it after a hundred yards, and stepped
off the platform into the road.

'There!' he said with a triumphant smile.
'I knew I could do the job. Any perishin'
fool can drive a bloomin' tram!'

'And 'oo the 'ell gave you leave to interfere?'
spluttered the breathless Horace, very heated
after his rapid progress. 'D' you want me to
lose me job?'

'This feller 'ere says I could 'ave a shot,'
said the sailor, pointing at the conductor.
'I never thought 'e could do it, 'Orace.
S'welp me, I didn't!'

'Any fool could do it!' snorted the man of
the sea.

'Calls me a fool, do yer?' snarled the driver.

'Tryin' to get me into trouble by runnin' off
with my tram '——

'Bloomin' thing ran off with me, mate!'

'No, it bloomin' well didn't. You did it
deliberate so that I should lose me job!
Look 'ere, now; if you ain't very careful, and
if you gets usin' any more o' your langidge, I
gives you in charge to the first bobby I sees.
You've bin interferin' wi' things wot doesn't
belong to you.'

'Oh, shut your jaw an' let's get a move on,
mate!' the sailor broke in, turning his back
and stumping laboriously up the steps to
rejoin his hilarious shipmates. 'I say, Bill,
ole dear! An' you too, 'Orace!' as his head
suddenly reappeared.

''Ullo! What d'yer want now?'

'Only to tell you that me an' my mates'll
stand you a wet when we gets to the town
station. Drive on, ole son!'

And away they went, and that was the last
I saw of them.

The pranks of ships' companies paid off from
their vessels after a long commission abroad
are sometimes beyond all comprehension. I
speak subject to correction, but I think it was
the men of Anson's squadron that captured
the Spanish treasure-ship who, on their arrival
in England in 1744 with their pockets bulging
with prize-money, celebrated their advent by
buying all the gold-laced hats, rich apparel,
and gold and silver watches in Plymouth.
Watches were expensive luxuries in those
days, but the joy of squandering their money

was not one whit mitigated by the fact that subsequently, in the lightness of their hearts, the men ruined their clothes and the watches by frying the latter over their galley fires during a drunken frolic.

Our present-day seamen would scarcely indulge in insane behaviour of this kind with their hardly earned shillings; but who would not be overflowing with good spirits and a general devil-may-care sort of feeling on stepping ashore for a month's or six weeks' leave after two or three years abroad?

At one time it was no rare thing for the men to celebrate the paying off of their ship by a farewell picnic, but a picnic on a gargantuan scale such as you and I have never taken part in. I once met one of these parties on the top of Portsdown Hill on their way to the place of entertainment. In fact, when I met them the entertainment was already in progress.

The day was a very hot one in midsummer, and the procession consisted of six char-à-bancs, each crammed to bursting with brazen-lunged, happy seamen; while a score of dusty, perspiring, and rather mournful-looking cyclists, for whom there was no room in the conveyances, brought up the rear. On the box-seat of each vehicle alongside the driver was an enormous barrel of beer, from which the company regaled themselves whenever they felt so disposed— which was often. Every now and then the cyclists, who evidently thought they were not receiving their fair share, pushed forward at full speed and refreshed themselves from the nearest char-à-banc whilst still pedalling furiously. Some of them fell off in the process, and narrowly avoided being run over.

Each vehicle had its own band in the shape of a medley of concertinas, mouth-organs, and banjos, and the sound of their triumphal progress, eked out by a vociferous vocal accompaniment, could have been heard for miles. Nevertheless, the outing was organised on proper naval lines, for all the vehicles flew the White Ensign in the stern, and the leading one flaunted an admiral's flag. The 'admiral' himself, a fat, bewhiskered, and raucous A.B., was perched on the box of his 'flagship,' whence, through lack of other signalling apparatus, in the intervals of liquid refreshment, he communicated his orders to the rest of the fleet by megaphone.

'Number two,' he howled, 'you 're astern o' station agen! Close up a bit, carn't you? An' tell them bloomin' deestroyers astern o' the line that if I sees 'em sprintin' ahead agen without my permission they 'll all 'ave their grog stopped!'

The 'destroyers,' needless to remark, were the men on bicycles.

I had noticed at once that each char-à-banc carried a 'boat' in the shape of a perambulator hung out on two spars representing davits, and presently I saw them put into use.

'Stan' by for general drill!' roared the flag-officer, balancing himself on the box, beer-mug in hand. 'Man overboard!'

The evolution must have been rehearsed beforehand, for immediately a man was hurled unceremoniously into the road from each vehicle, and amid shouts of 'Stop engines!' and wild yells of excitement from the men of the squadron, the cortège pulled up, the perambulators were lowered, and, with a man in charge of each, the 'men overboard' were rescued and restored to their seats.

'Not 'arf smart enough!' was the 'admiral's' strident comment. 'Number four! when I sings out, "Man overboard!" I means man overboard! He ain't allowed to get out and walk abart as he perishin' well likes!'

So the 'boats' were hoisted again, and the exercise was repeated.

The next item on the programme was, 'Away all boat's crews; pull round the fleet!' when each perambulator, occupied by the largest man they could find in each char-à-banc, and propelled by the smallest, had to be pushed at a racing pace the whole way round the line of vehicles and back to its own 'ship,' cheered on by a chorus of full-throated yells from the delighted spectators. This over, the cortège presently resumed its bacchanal progress, in single line ahead at six knots, with musical honours, the 'destroyers' having previously been ordered to take station in the van, where the 'admiral' could keep his horny and unsympathetic eye upon them and limit their consumption of fuel. And so they went on their way rejoicing, until their piercing yells died away in the distance.

That picnic was strictly a men's function. There were no ladies present.

Perhaps, if the *Triptolemus* survives this war, our people also will have their picnic when the ship pays off. But I hardly think so, beer is such a precious commodity in these days, and a sailors' picnic without malt liquor must be like pork without crackling.

CHAPTER IV.

SHIP'S COMPANY.

I.

THE ship's company of the *Triptolemus* are 'Duffoes,' which peculiar nickname —pronounced 'Duff'-oes,' and derived from 'duff,' the nautical term for a pudding—means that they hail from 'Guzzle,' or the West Country. Why crews drafted to ships from the Royal Naval Barracks at Devonport should have such reputations for gluttony I have never discovered. I think it is a libel, for I have yet to learn that West Country sailormen are fonder of their victuals than those from 'Pompey' (Portsmouth), or 'Chats' (Chatham), or than Scotsmen, Irishmen, or Welshmen. They all seem to have equally healthy appetites, except perhaps when the ship happens to be in a gale of wind and a heavy sea. Then, I am forced to admit, some of them become as pale and as limp as pocket-handkerchiefs, and do not really much care whether it is Christmas or Easter.

Our ship commissioned some three years after the outbreak of war, so that the men, like the officers, have been brought together from the four corners of the earth. Their war record, therefore, is a surprising one; for some have served in battleships, some in battle-cruisers and light cruisers, and still

more in destroyers and other small craft all
over the world. Indeed, there is hardly a
naval engagement or operation of this war in
which some one or other has not taken part.
We have men who fought in that brilliant
little action in the Heligoland Bight on 28th
August 1914; others who were present at
the sinking of the *Blücher* by Sir David
Beatty's battle-cruisers in January 1915; and
still more who were in destroyers at Jutland.
We have even a man who saw the sinking
of the *Good Hope* and the *Monmouth* on that
eventful evening off Coronel, and several who
were with Sir Doveton Sturdee at the final
defeat of Von Spee off the Falklands. There
are others who were in Gallipoli, or have
served in the Cameroons, in the naval operations in East Africa, in one of the British
ships present at the capture of Tsingtau by the
Japanese, with the gunboats in Mesopotamia,
or in destroyers and monitors under the fire
of the German guns on the Belgian coast. I
only wish they could be induced to describe
some of their varied experiences, for, if the
Censor would permit them to be published—
which I doubt—their yarns would be well
worth listening to, and would provide ample
material for a dozen books.

As a matter of fact, our men are not all
West-Countrymen. We have a small proportion of 'hostility-men'—men who have
joined the Royal Navy for three years or the
duration of the war. There are no 'con-
scripts' among them. They are volunteers;

and, among others, we have a Welsh school-master, a North Country miner, a Yorkshire police-constable, an architect's pupil, and a young man who owns what he politely terms a 'licensed victualler's business.' The 'victuals' he refers to, I have since discovered, are mainly liquid. There is also the man who was apprenticed to a coffin-maker, but now spends his time in doing odd carpentry jobs on board when he is not engaged in more seaman-like occupations.

Our hostility-men were rather strange to the life at first, and certainly, being provided with a naval uniform, and then being sent to a destroyer after a short spell of training at a shore depot, must have been a startling revelation to all of them. They were a never-failing source of wonderment to the more mature members of the ship's company. The ways and expressions of the navy were a mystery to them. They talked about 'going downstairs,' and the 'front' and the 'back' of the ship instead of the bow and the stern. They became fearfully and wonderfully sea-sick, so that folk who were ordinarily seasick gazed at them in mute astonishment, thought themselves wonderful sea-dogs, and thanked their lucky stars that it was possible to be worse than they themselves were. But the hearts of our hostility-men are in the right place, nevertheless, and it was surprising how rapidly they became acclimatised to their new surroundings, and how soon they seemed to fit into the general scheme of things.

Fortunately for our peace of mind, we are not burdened with anybody with an impediment in his speech; for there is a story—let us hope it is only a story—of a certain hostility-man with a rather liquid and very pronounced stammer who was sent to sea in one of the more elderly destroyers. He could not talk without stammering, though he could sing without the least difficulty. Indeed, I believe he had been a choir-boy at some period of his career.

It so happened that the destroyer was in a heavy sea, and that the cook, on emerging from his galley to empty a bucket of refuse, was incontinently swept overboard by a wave. Considerable consternation on the part of the hostility-man, who, unused to such tragical happenings, was rather perplexed as to what to do.

He saw that the rapid emergence of the cook had not been noticed from the bridge, and hesitated for a moment, trying to make up his mind to leap overboard and save him; but the sight of the raging, wind-swept sea daunted him. He recollected he was not a strong swimmer, particularly in sea-boots and an oilskin, so decided that discretion was the better part of valour, and made his way forward to the bridge.

'P-p-p-please, sir!' he managed to get out, accosting the commanding-officer—' ck-ck-ck-ck-cook '——

'Sing it, man! For the Lord's sake, sing it!' the skipper interrupted, aware of the man's infirmity, and anxious to hear what he had to say.

The hostility-man lifted up his voice. 'P-p-please, sir, cookie's gone overboard, bucket and all!' he carolled, fitting the words to the tune of 'The Campbells are Coming!'

Poor cookie! He must have been at least two miles astern by the time his loss became known!

The seven officers in the wardroom have had careers as varied as those of some of the men. One of us was present at the battle of the Falklands, and no less than three served in the Dardanelles. Even our 'snotty,' the midshipman R.N.V.R., was blooded before he joined the navy; for at an age when most of his brothers were at school, he was driving an ambulance-car attached to a British Red Cross unit serving on the Italian front. But the doctor, who before the war was still a medical student, and who, when hostilities are over, will have to return to a London hospital to complete his studies, has had the most hair-raising adventures of us all. Since the outbreak of war he has spent no small portion of his time in a destroyer in the North Sea, where he was present at the engagement on the Dogger Bank in January 1915, and has taken part in various altercations with German destroyers and shore batteries off the Belgian coast, and other little sea-bickerings which have never seen the light of day in the newspapers, and will find no mention in any official history of the war.

But the greatest adventure of all was when
his ship was torpedoed by a submarine far out
in the Atlantic.   The vessel, broken in halves
by two successive explosions, sank like a
stone, and before he quite realised what was
happening the doctor found himself struggling
in the water with an injured man. Together
they swam to an overturned boat, and, on
being joined by other survivors, presently
succeeded in righting her.   Having bailed her
comparatively free of water, they next rescued
various of their shipmates, until finally there
were some twenty-four men and the ship's
pet-dog huddled on board.   The remainder
of the crew had been killed or had gone down
with the ship.

During this time the submarine came to
the surface, and, after the pleasing habit of
German submarines, pointed guns and rifles
at the helpless survivors, and ordered the captain and the senior engineer to come on board
as prisoners.   The two officers swam across,
and nothing more was heard of them until,
many weeks later, their relatives received the
welcome news that they were alive and well
in a prison camp in Germany.   The U-boat,
after refusing to part with any water or provisions, steamed off on the surface.

Those in the boat were left with three oars,
a tattered oilskin, the clothes they stood up
in, a small quantity of biscuit, and a minute
amount of water.   They had no compass ;
and when the submarine left them to their
almost inevitable fate they were between one

hundred and forty and one hundred and fifty miles from the nearest land !

Try to realise the feelings of our twenty-two on finding themselves alone on the broad ocean ! They were wet through to the skin, and the weather was unsettled. They were a long way from the coast, and though perhaps with due economy their food might last them for the journey—the biscuit ration worked out at one and a half biscuits per man per day— they had no more water than would serve to put each man on an allowance of two table-spoonfuls every twenty-four hours.

It is easy enough to sit down and describe what happened, but no words of mine can ever express the mental and physical agony of the terrible ordeal through which that devoted little band passed. They shaped their course eastward, steering by the sun, stars, and the prevailing westerly wind ; and hour after hour, day after day, they relieved each other at the oars, and utilised the oilskin as a sail whenever the wind was favourable. Three times they were overtaken by heavy Atlantic gales, when the gigantic, white-capped seas, rolling in from the west with all the might of the open ocean behind them, threatened to fill and overwhelm the boat. At times they lay to with a sea-anchor over the bows, bailing for their lives to keep the water under. Sometimes they scudded before it with their rag of a sail set, while a man sat on the stern-post to take the brunt of the curling seas on his back, and so prevent the boat from being swamped.

I know those gigantic Atlantic rollers, and even from the deck of a good-sized ship they obliterate the horizon.

Once, on the second day, the poor fellows sighted the smoke of a steamer, but the ship passed them by at a distance of three miles without seeing them. Hour after hour that boat struggled doggedly to the eastward. The nights, though it was summer, were bitterly cold, so that the survivors, wet to the skin and numb to the marrow, huddled together for a little warmth, hardly expecting to see another sunrise. The days when the sun shone were overpoweringly hot, and their throats became so parched and swollen for want of water that they could swallow nothing in the way of food except a little chewed biscuit. To alleviate their thirst they licked the dew from the thwarts and gunwales until their noses and chins were blistered and raw. Two men, delirious from exposure and thirst, drank sea-water, and died horrible deaths.

And for eight mortal days they struggled on, their strength failing rapidly and their scanty stock of water ebbing lower and lower. The two table-spoonfuls of water were reduced to one. The end must have seemed very near —but still they struggled on.

Then, at daylight on one never-to-be-forgotten morning, the sun rose in a cloudless sky to display a thin purple smear on the eastern horizon. It was the land, fifteen miles distant, and, with a supreme thankfulness surging in their hearts, the exhausted men rowed towards it with what strength remained in their famished bodies. Before long a breeze sprang up from the west, and they hoisted their improvised sail to assist them on their way, so that eventually, just before sundown, the twenty men and the ship's dog landed at a certain lighthouse. Their faces, hands, and feet were blistered and swollen to twice their normal size by sun and sea-water, and they were so weak with fatigue that they could barely crawl on all fours up the steps cut in the rock.

They were cared for by the kind-hearted keepers, and in due course returned to the civilisation they had never expected to see again—returned to read their obituary notices in the newspapers. They had lived to tell the tale; they had won through by what must have seemed a miracle, though there is no denying that the miracle could never have happened but for the dogged grit and persistence of the men concerned. Many people would have lost their spirits and given up the impossible task in despair; but those men did not. Their attitude in the face of almost certain death was typically British. They refused to acknowledge themselves beaten until the end actually came, and, assisted by a merciful Providence, succeeded in worrying through in the face of almost insurmountable dangers and difficulties.

The doctor's attitude towards the whole experience is surprisingly light-hearted. He admits that he was ' a bit hungry ' and ' devilish

thirsty,' and that his hands and bare feet were
swollen to twice their usual size when he
landed.   After a lot of questioning, he says
that the gales were 'pretty putrid,' and that
his boatmates and himself were 'beastly wet
and uncomfortable' the whole time.   But
never once have I heard him utter a word of
complaint, and he seems to consider the
adventure of his life in much the same way as
an ordinary person regards a long and uncomfortable railway journey.   Indeed, he appears
to treat the whole ghastly business rather as a
joke, and tells us in his humorous way that
the only size of boots he could wear on his
return were No. 10's.   He also remembers
that some one had been mixing a drum of
liquid red-lead just before the ship was
torpedoed, and that the explosion, hurling the
contents into the air in a shower, dyed one
man a vivid scarlet from head to foot.

'He had a deuce of a bleat,' is the doctor's
version.   'He couldn't get the stuff out of his
skin and hair for toffee, and still looked like a
Red Indian when he got ashore.'

He may have, but nevertheless I take off
my hat to him and the rest of the party.

Our first trip to sea, on our way to our base
from the port where the ship was built, was
altogether uneventful.   It was summer, and
the weather was fine throughout the journey,
while the ship behaved like a perfect lady.
We had blue sky, a hot sun, and a smooth
sea.   There were none of the wild caperings,
the skittish prancings, the heavy lurchings,

and the frantic wrigglings which afterwards characterised her behaviour in heavy weather, so that, during the early portion of our maiden passage, some of our intrepid mariners, those hostility-men who had never been at sea before, were lulled into a sense of false security, and were quite ready to believe that a sailor's life was a happy one.

They were very proud and very war-like. They stood on the forecastle in knots, with their trousers flapping in the breeze, gazing into the middle distance for the first signs of a hostile sub-marine. They were thoroughly nautical. They recollected with some pride that they were now 'handy little lads in navy blue,' 'boys of the bulldog breed,' and all the rest of it. They be-longed to the  band of lucky, care-free individuals who are supposed only to have to walk down a street with a deep-sea roll, carefully assumed for the occasion, to set all the female hearts a-flutter-ing with gladness.

The bluejacket is a lucky fellow. It is his loose trousers, his saucy jumper, and the rakish angle of his cap 'as does it.' As for me—well, I notice that when I stay in an hotel in uniform, short-sighted people are sometimes apt to take me for the hall-porter or some equally important personage. Several times I have been ordered to whistle for a taxi. Once I was the proud recipient of a silver sixpence; while the last time I was in Edinburgh I received a severe censure from a lady old enough to be my grandmother because the lift did not start the moment she stepped into it.

'It is a positive disgrace that I should be kept waiting like this!' she observed, glaring at me very fiercely.

'I quite agree,' said I with my sweetest smile.

She still glared, evidently making up her mind to report me to the management for incivility, or to ask why I was not in khaki. But she did neither. The situation was saved by the arrival of the lift-attendant; whereupon the old lady, after examining me critically through a pair of opera-glasses on a stick, observed that she was sorry for the mistake, but that it was a pity our uniforms were so much alike. So all was peace.

It is surprising how unfamiliar His Majesty's naval uniform seems to be. I was once in a crowded carriage in a London tube, and noticed a small boy opposite eyeing me with great curiosity.

'Muvver!' he at length summoned up the courage to ask in a shrill falsetto, extending a finger in my direction—'muvver! what's that man?'

'Hush, dear!' said the fond parent in a very audible whisper. 'Hush, Charlie! ' Don't point. That pretty gentleman's got something to do with a railway!'

It was the first time in my life I had ever been called pretty!

But all this has nothing whatsoever to do with the *Triptolemus*.

Throughout the morning our hostility-men were feeling extremely seaman-like. I wonder they didn't dance upon the deck, slap their fronts and backs, and shout, 'Yo—heave—ho!' whatever that may mean, in approved nautical style.

But alas for their happiness! Towards two o'clock in the afternoon we drew out from under the lee of the land, and began to steam to the northward at twenty-two knots, with a gentle Atlantic swell broad on our port beam. It was nothing as swells go, but the ship started to roll gently from side to side as she settled down into her stride. And ten minutes later, happening to glance aft, I saw one of the newly joined ones suspiciously close to the ship's side. He was presently joined by another, then another, and another, until at last there were six of them. Their faces were pale green, and their expressions miserable. Their demeanour was utterly sad. There was very little of the bulldog about them; they merely grasped the rail, bowed down their heads, and—words fail me. They are better now, for that was over six months ago.

They afterwards had the temerity to inform one of the older members of the ship's company, an elderly A.B., who has been in the service for many a year, and is very much of a sea-dog, that it was merely the unusual smell of the oil-fuel which had upset them.

'Garn!' said the A.B., with a snort of contempt. 'D'ye mean to say you've bin brought up on vi'lets?'

However, the next day we arrived at our base, where we were at once ordered to proceed alongside an oiler to replenish our depleted supply of oil. Those who go down to the sea in oil-burning ships have several reasons to be thankful. For one thing, they are strangers to that horrible feeling that every mile steamed, every increase of speed, means so many more tons of coal to be embarked on arrival at the journey's end. And just think of the labour which coaling ship entails! The collier comes alongside, and every ounce of coal taken from her holds has to be shovelled by hand into bags holding a couple of hundredweights. Then, when ten such bags have been filled, they are hooked to the end of a wire whip, hurtled through space, and deposited upon the man-of-war's deck; and woe betide the people responsible if that whip is kept waiting! On their arrival the bags are unhooked and separated, and when each one has been placed on a wheel-barrow, it is trundled off by a perspiring

The greater number of us can retire below and go to sleep.

PAGE 71.

person to the bunker-opening, which may be several hundred feet distant. The contents are then tipped below by more men; while stokers, grovelling in the black depths of the bunkers, trim the coal as it descends in a cascade. Except for the actual hoisting, the operation is all done by manual labour; so it is weary and back-breaking work. But many ships have coaled, on an average, once a week or more ever since this war started.

In an oil-fired ship we simply go alongside an oiler, or an oiler comes alongside us, a hose or two is connected up, a pump in the oiler's interior heaves round, and the oil is driven into our tanks. We merely have a couple of men to attend the hoses, and to scream, 'Stop 'er!' at the pitch of their lungs when each tank is nearly full. There is none of the shovelling, the hoisting, the trundling about in barrows, and the tipping of the coal into the bunkers. Merely the oil flowing quietly through a pipe; so that the greater number of us can retire below and go to sleep.

At sea, too, the vessel burning coal has to have the necessary steam generated in her boilers by squads of stokers, who do little else but fling shovelful after shovelful of fuel into the glowing furnaces. They have to keep it up for the whole of a four-hour watch; then eight hours' rest—four only if the ship is steaming at high speed—then back to the stokehold again for more shovelling.

Think, too, of the number of men necessary to do the work. In an oil-fired ship the

steam, and hence the speed, are regulated by
the number of sprayers alight in the furnaces,
and the oil is simply pumped through these
sprayers in a thin, flaming film, like gas through
a jet. If more steam is required, a man simply
turns on another sprayer or two, and the thing
is done. There is no shovelling. One man
can look after one of our boilers, but if we
burned coal two or three would be required
for the same purpose. So the difference in
the stokehold complement of an oil-fired and
a coal-burning ship of the same tonnage is very
marked. The latter will probably carry about
three times as many stokers as the former.

There is another advantage, in that the oil-
ship, with due care, can travel at full speed
with little more than a thin vapour showing
from her funnels. The coal ship cannot. She
sometimes vomits forth a black pall which is
visible for miles. It is impossible to prevent it.

But lest we become proud, it is as well to
remember that there are such things as coal-
burning vessels, and that one day we may
again be serving in them. One oil-burning
battleship, indeed, has a burnished shovel hung
up in a conspicuous place on the quarter-deck
to serve as a reminder; and on the business
portion of that shovel are the words, ' LEST
WE FORGET.' It is good advice.

Even with the simple operation of oiling we
sometimes have regrettable incidents. Hoses
have been known to burst, with the result
that the coco-nut matting on the upper deck

has been well saturated with evil-smelling oil-fuel the colour and consistency of treacle, while our nice gray side has become striped like a zebra. This generally leads to strife between the first lieutenant, who is responsible for the cleanliness of the ship, and the chief stoker, who isn't, but who superintends the fuelling arrangements.

Sometimes the brazen-lunged gentleman watching the filling of our tanks omits to shout at the right moment to the man at the pump in the oiler, with the consequence that the tank may overflow. But even in one's cabin one is generally aware if something is amiss.

There comes the strident shout of 'Stop 'er!'

They evidently don't.

Then 'Stop 'er! STOP 'ER! STOP 'ER!' in a rapid, howling crescendo, followed by sundry remarks about 'blank-flanged purple perishers who are blinkin' well asleep,' addressed to some gentleman in the oiler.

This generally means more oil on the deck, and more 'What the devil?' and 'Who the devil?' on the part of Number One, followed invariably by the final remark, 'Well, go and get some waste and mop it up, and report to me when it's done!'

Once, in our very palmy days, when we were particularly anxious to oil as quickly as possible, we secured alongside an oiler in record time and got the hoses on board.

'Heave round!' said the chief stoker, and

they hove round. At last, after half-an-hour, it was discovered that one of the hoses had produced no oil at all, and that the tank concerned was as empty as when we had started.

'Heave round!' said the chief stoker.

'We are heaving!' replied the man in the oiler.

'No, you're not!'

'Yes, we are!'

'Well, there's something the matter with your bloomin' pump!'

'No, there isn't!'

'Yes, there must be! We're not gettin' a drop of oil this end into the tank!'

'Pump's all right!' from the oiler.

'Something's bloomin' well the matter!' observed the chief stoker, scratching his head.

Something was. The cap was still on the end of the hose—our end!

One of our oil-tanks happens to be underneath the engineer's storeroom, which, like other engineers' storerooms, contains a small lathe, and various cupboards crammed with tools, such as hammers, saws, spanners, wrenches, files, chisels, screw-drivers, taps and dies, &c., as well as nuts, bolts, screws, brass and copper wire, sheet copper and brass, and a hundred and ten other things which I cannot enumerate, but all of which are necessary to keep the ship in running order. The store, in fact, is like the ironmongery department of the Army and Navy Stores on a small scale.

The storekeeper, Stoker Petty Officer Martin,

who looks after all these things, is a bit of a potentate in his way. He is the king of the castle, and if anybody wants a cold chisel for chopping a wire hawser, a saw for dividing a spar, a gimlet to drill a hole, or a piece of sheet-tin to make a new top for the galley stove-pipe, he is the man to go to. Sometimes, as he regards seamen as fellows of the baser sort who use his wood-chisels for scraping the ship's side, and who have a happy knack of losing overboard things which do not belong to them—an opinion which is not altogether unmerited—not all the wild horses of Assyria will make him disgorge a single tool—but that is another matter.

What I do wish to point out is that Martin is the monarch of the storeroom. He has burnished the steel deck until it is like a skating-rink, has covered the walls with the best enamel filched privily from the first lieutenant, and has hung photographs of his wife, children, and female relations, in fretwork frames made in his spare time, wherever there is room for them. The storeroom is his kingdom, and when we go the rounds at divisions on Sunday he takes a great pride in pointing out its beauty spots.

But underneath the storeroom there is an oil-tank, and when we go alongside an oiler the hose comes down through the hatch in the deck above and passes into the tank through a small, brass-rimmed opening in the floor. Perhaps you have never heard the story of Chivers.

1. And it came to pass that the King's storekeeper, the stoker petty officer who is called Martin, was once granted seven days' leave to visit his ailing grandmother, who lived in Devon. And one named Chivers, a leading stoker, reigned temporarily in his stead.

2. Now Chivers was an idle fellow who had not learned the ways of storekeepers. He did not know the first thing about the keeping of the King's stores, and still less about the embarkation of oil-fuel.

3. And when the ship went alongside the oiler for to replenish her supply of fuel, for she had lately returned from business in great waters, the hose was passed below into the tank which is beneath the King's storeroom. And Chivers inserted the end of the hose through the opening in the floor to a depth of three inches, whereas he should have inserted it to three times three inches.

4. And he lifted up his voice and said, Heave round!

5. Those in the oiler heard him, and hove round. Yea, with incredible speed did they heave round the pump, so that there was an exceeding great pressure.

6. And Chivers, thinking his work completed for a while, departed to the deck and lighted him a cigarette. Yea, he even puffed smoke from his lips and stood regarding the scenery.

7. And presently there came to his ears a mighty sound of splashing as of great waters in a whirlpool. But he considered it not, for it conveyed nothing to him.

8. But after the space of five minutes he approached the storeroom, saying, We will now see how much oil hath entered into the tank, for, verily, I believe it to be nearly filled.

9. And, lo! the hose, leaping from the opening with the pressure, had filled the storeroom to a depth of four feet and more, so that the storeroom was even like unto the North Sea, which is shallow. And

great had been the splashing thereof, for the cupboards even were filled with oil, and the walls, and the ceiling; and the pictures of the storekeeper's female relations were likewise covered. And great was the damage in that place.

10. And Chivers lifted up his voice and howled like a dog which is in the wilderness, Stop 'er! Stop er! But they stopped her not; so that Chivers also was covered with oil. Yea, he even bathed in it up to his armpits.

11. But soon, hearing the lamentation which was in the storeroom, those on deck looked below and saw the evil thing which had come to pass, and laughing together at Chivers's calamity, they commanded those in the oiler to stop the pump. And the pump was stopped.

12. And the young men that were gathered round in an exceeding great multitude made mock of Chivers, saying, What manner of man art thou who hast done this thing? Yea, verily, thou wilt catch it hot and strong from the keeper of the King's storeroom when he returneth from his business.

13. But Chivers did not laugh. He lifted up his voice and wept, so that the tears of salt mingled with the oil that was upon his countenance.

14. And presently there came the master and the engineer of the ship, who fell upon Chivers with an exceeding great wrath, saying, What manner of fool art thou? See what damage thou hast done! See what oil thou hast wasted! Dost thou not know there is a famine of oil in the land? Yea, verily, thou art a thrice-cursed fool, and shalt pay for the damage that thou hast done.

15. And it came to pass that another man was set to reign in Chivers's stead, and that Chivers was suffered to repair some of the damage that he had done. But yet he could not repair all the damage, for when the storekeeper returned from his wanderings in the land of Devon his storeroom

L.S.   F

was like unto nothing which is on earth or in heaven. Oil was lodged in all its crevices. Yea, the oil even dripped from the roof for many days, so that the paint and the features of the storekeeper's female relations were permanently obliterated.

16. And the storekeeper lifted up his voice with an exceeding great wrath and cursed Chivers, saying unto him, Thou art not a man. Thou art a fool. I reposed my trust in thee, but thou hast been found wanting. Get thee hence quickly, lest I am overcome by my wrath and do thee an injury.

17. And Chivers made excuses, saying, O King, live for ever! Lo! it was not my fault, but the fault of them who live in the oiler. Give me time, I pray thee, and I will repair the damage that I have done.

18. But the King rolled his eyes and said, Get thee hence, lest I smite thee upon the mouth or upon the ears, or lay my foot upon thy body.

19. And Chivers departed thence with much lamentation and wailing, and was no more suffered to enter into the King's storeroom.

20. And the company that were assembled in the ship laughed him to scorn, and made mock of him for many months, calling after him in the public places, Ya, ya! here cometh he who oileth the King's storeroom.

21. But Chivers turned his face and answered them not, for he was ashamed. He threw dust upon his head and mingled his bread with weeping. Verily I say unto you, Chivers is a fool.

CHAPTER V.

I.

IT was one of those blustery days in January, with a dull, overcast sky, and a stiff breeze which tore the tops off the short, leaden-coloured seas. It was not really rough as roughness goes, for we were drawing in under the lee of the land, with wind and sea on the quarter, so that there was hardly any movement, merely an almost imperceptible roll, which was more comforting than otherwise after the buffeting we had experienced outside.

We were humming along at something over twenty knots to get into harbour before dark, anxious as ever for a little peace and quietness after eight-and-forty hours of activity which it is scarcely advisable to specify. Our weather had been as bad as it possibly could be. It had been blowing half a gale of wind for some days, which, out in the open water, raised an angry, curling sea, which broke on board as we crashed and thumped into it, and sent sheets and showers of spray hurtling high over the bridge and the funnels. The thermometer had been well down towards zero, and on leaving the bridge on our eventual arrival in harbour my eyebrows were frozen stiff.

We were all rather looking forward to a square meal and something hot to drink. Personally, I fancied nothing better than tea with a soft-boiled egg—if the steward could produce one—followed by a hot bath, a change of raiment, and forty winks in an arm-chair in front of a blazing stove. One does attach an undue importance to such little luxuries when one is cold and wet, and has been cold and wet for nearly two days. Most of us had been on deck the greater portion of the time, and nobody in his senses likes dodging seas and snow-flurries. They always seem to get the better of one, and finish up by trickling gently down the back of one's neck and into one's sea-boots.

But the North Sea in winter is always an inhospitable place for the destroyer. It has only two advantages that I can think of. First, one may tumble up against something hostile about the size of one's own ship; second, bad weather makes one supremely grateful for the more or less civilised amenities of life in harbour, even if one has no long bath and has to perform one's ablutions in a thing like a glorified saucer.

A little ship that flashed past us was starting, poor little thing! for her everlasting patrol, steaming off into the night and the wild, wind-swept turbulence we had just left. She was travelling head to sea, walloping along with the water sweeping over her low turtle-back and the spray flying across her deck. Her funnels were caked white with the sea-salt of previous patrols. Her side was a futurist picture of dirty gray paint, black blotches, and streaks and patches of red rust. Her decks were indescribably filthy.

What could one expect? She had no time to indulge in the luxury of cleanliness. Her routine was forty-eight hours on patrol and forty-eight hours off, though of the 'stand-off' period she spent at least twelve hours in getting back into harbour, coaling ship, drawing stores and provisions, and returning afterwards to her beat. Her only real leisure came during her four-monthly refits and the four-day intervals for boiler-cleaning once every four or five weeks, when her weary men sometimes gave her a scrub and a lick of paint.

A burly, oil-skinned figure on her bridge waved as she sped by, and we waved back. She passed so close that looking down on to her deck, with its little group of men clustered for shelter under the lee of the foremost funnel, felt like being in the gallery of a theatre. Compared with our ship, she seemed a veritable pigmy; though, goodness knows, we are no giant, merely a vessel of a little more than a thousand tons displacement. She was perhaps a third of this size.

A thick cloud of pungent black smoke from her stumpy funnels came drifting across our bridge, and incidentally put a fat and rather hot 'stoker'* in the first-lieutenant's eye.

* 'Stoker,' a naval slang term for a cinder or a smut.

'Ten million devils!' he ejaculated, reviling the cause of his discomfiture and producing a sodden handkerchief. 'She's been and gone and bunged up my starboard optic!'

'Poor chaps!' said I, thinking of different things as I watched her plunging and staggering in our heavy wash. 'She'll get the very deuce of a dusting outside!'

I watched her until she disappeared into the gathering gloom to seaward, into the dark, wind-tortured waste whence we had come.

And a couple of hours later, by which time we were safely secured to our buoy, and the boiled egg and the hot bath were things of the past, I thought of her as I sat in front of a roaring stove and listened through the open scuttle to the whistling of the wind and the sound of the vicious little waves slapping up against our hull. I shivered as I imagined her all alone on her solitary beat, where the sea leapt and played in such fury, and those blinding snow-squalls came sweeping down from windward; I thought of those on board her, and felt rather sympathetic, for I have served in craft of her type, and am painfully aware of their behaviour in a heavy sea.

For she, you must understand, was an old 'thirty knotter,'* a relic of a bygone age that, but for the war, might long since have found herself on the scrap-heap or figuring on a

* 'Thirty knotter,' the general service term applied to a certain type of destroyer built between about 1897 and 1901. They were the successors of the first T.B.D.'s ever built, the old 'twenty-seven knotters' first constructed in 1893-94.

For she, you must understand, was a relic of a bygone age.

Page 82.

dockyard sale list. She was launched in 1899, and looked it.

Those who go down to the sea in big destroyers, the thousand and twelve hundred tonners of to-day, may regard her with kindly amusement, mingled with a little pity, as they pass her by; but the fact remains that she and dozens of her sisters have done yeoman service ever since that fateful day in 1914 when a Teutonic War Lord set the whole of Europe ablaze. And she and the others of the Old Brigade will continue to do this work until the War Lord is brought to reason, or their engines drop out through their bottoms, or until they are blown up on mines, hurled ashore in a gale of wind, or disintegrated in some other equally violent and disagreeable fashion. But Fritz, the submarine, thinks twice before he approaches them, for they have many pairs of sharp young eyes, and carry nasty stings, which they are only too delighted to use.

The name of the little ship that passed us that evening was the *Cyclone*, and it is her life-story that I propose to tell.

II.

When pretty Miss Katherine Trevelyan, the only daughter of old Admiral Sir Roger Trevelyan, was asked to launch a destroyer from the contractors' yard where she had been built, she was accounted a very lucky girl. She was certainly very proud, for it was a great honour to be asked to launch a man-of-war, even so small a man-of-war as a destroyer; while Katherine, though not at all mercenary, was quite well enough versed in nautical matters to be aware that the firm who built a vessel sometimes presented the lady of the launch with a memento in the shape of a brooch or a bracelet.

So on a brilliant June morning in the last year but one of the reign of Queen Victoria, Katherine, dressed all in white, with her mother, her father, and quite a number of her relations, besides many of the firm's bigwigs in top-hats, frock-coats, and with white flowers in their button-holes, stood upon a gaily decorated platform erected in front of the new destroyer's sharp bows as she lay on the building-slip. The girl, if the truth be known, felt rather shy and nervous. She had never before taken part in any public function, and the dense crowd of sight-seers clustered on each side of the slip now seemed to be doing nothing but gaze up at her with curious eyes.

But the crowd approved of her, neverthe-less. In the enclosure below, reserved for the firm's senior employees and their families, stood Mrs Barnby, the wife of old Ezra Barnby, the foreman of shipwrights. He was a man of over sixty, who had served the firm for forty years, and had played no small part in the building of the ship now about to be launched. But torpedo-craft of all kinds were newfangled inventions little to his liking. Indeed, he could quite well remember the days when ships were generally built of wood.

'Who is the young leddy this time, Ezra?' Mrs Barnby asked, settling her small bonnet firmly on her gray head and producing a handkerchief.

Mrs Barnby, it must be understood, was a connoisseur in the matter of launches. She made a point of never missing one, for, as a Mrs Foreman of Shipwrights and the proud mother of four sons in the same trade, she was a leading figure in local shipyard society.

'Name o' Trevelyan,' her man told her. 'Her father's admiral. He must be the ole gent wi' the red face an' the white whiskers standin' beside the gal.'

'Poor lamb!' said his wife sympathetically, looking up at the platform and guessing Katherine's feelings. 'She does look a little slip of a thing, and that shy with all the people.'

'A bonny bit of a gal, all th' same, Bess,' was Mr Barnby's approving comment; and Mr Barnby was right.

On the platform overhead, the senior member of the firm, with his hat removed, was instructing Katherine in her new duties. Suspended in front of her from two silken cords was a bottle of Australian wine, decorated with red and white flowers and leaves, and pulling it towards him, he placed it in her hands.

'You must break it against the ship's stem,' he explained; 'and then you christen the ship by name.'

'I understand,' she nodded, her eyes shining

with excitement. 'I've learnt it all up.— Father, hold my parasol, please.'

'Be careful you smash the bottle first shot, my Kit,' murmured the old sea-dog in a very audible whisper, tucking the sunshade under his arm like a telescope. 'Damn bad luck if you don't, so'——

'Hush, Roger!' in a horrified undertone from his wife. 'You really mustn't use language like that in front of all these people!'

The admiral seemed mildly surprised. 'Language!' he said. 'But what the'——

''S-sh, Roger! Be quiet!'

Katherine had taken the flower-decked bottle in both hands, and was poising it for the swing. She hesitated a moment, holding it aloft, and then dashed it forward with all her young strength. It struck fair across the sharp stem of the ship with a thud and a crash of breaking glass. A few pieces tinkled on to the concrete below, and a frothing trickle of wine went flowing down the cut-water.

'I christen you *Cyclone!*' said Miss Katherine Trevelyan in her clear voice, stepping well to the front of the platform. 'Success to you, and to all who sail in you!'

It was said very prettily, and some one started a cheer, which was taken up by person after person, group after group, until the great volume of sound went rolling out across the river. Then the throng of spectators suddenly went mad, and became transformed into a sea of waving hats and fluttering handkerchiefs. Kitty bowed. Her cheeks were blazing. She was being cheered for the first time in her life.

'Well done, Kit, my gal!' came a hoarse whisper from her father when at length the turmoil had subsided. 'It quite reminds me of the old—— Eh; what's that you're saying, Jane?' turning to his wife, who was trying to whisper into his ear. 'Lunch!' he burst out. 'Of course we do. They asked us, didn't they? Damme, ain't I a shareholder, Jane?'

Lady Trevelyan suddenly became the colour of a peony. But the senior member of the firm was busy doing conjuring tricks, for in some mysterious manner best known to himself he had produced a large morocco case stamped in gold with Katherine's initials. He opened it carefully, to display a carved oaken mallet and a silver-bladed chisel nestling side by side on the white velvet lining.

'Take these, please,' he said, thrusting the implements into her hands. 'You see that red-silk cord stretched across the block of wood in front of you?'

'Yes.'

'Put the edge of the chisel on it—yes, like that—and when I tell you, give it a sharp tap with the mallet. When that rope is cut it releases a sort of wedge which frees the ship and allows her to slide into the water. Are you all ready?'

'Yes,' said Kitty, waiting with the mallet raised.

'Cut, please!' ordered the senior member.

And Kitty, determined there should be no mistake about it, smote with such vigour that the chisel was left quivering in the block of wood as the severed rope flicked away into space.

There came a crash as the dog-shores fell away, and then, after a moment's hesitation, the slender black hull of the *Cyclone* started to move slowly and silently down the incline. There was a short silence, followed by a shout of 'She's off!' then a deafening roar of cheering, and more waving of hats and handkerchiefs.

Faster and faster she travelled, until, with a splash and a splutter of spray, her rudder and her twin-propellers took the water together. Next her stern lifted as it became waterborne, and the uproar became even more deafening as the tugs in the river chimed into the babel with piercing blasts from their steam-whistles.

In another moment the bows of the ship were free of the launching-ways and she was floating in her element, gliding rapidly into the centre of the stream with the momentum, with her White Ensign and the Union Flag fluttering bravely in the breeze. Then her speed lessened as one by one the securing hawsers took the strain, until at last she lay motionless on the bosom of the river; while waiting tugs, with their fussy paddles churning the muddy water into foam, went alongside to take their newly born sister to the jetty, where she would presently be completed for sea.

The tumult gradually subsided.

Kitty watched the tugs as they grappled the destroyer and swung her round. Her heart was very full, for she felt, somehow, as if the ship belonged to her. She did, indeed, for Katherine was her godmother.

'You did it remarkably well, Miss Trevelyan,' said the senior member, wrenching the chisel from its resting-place. 'Never saw a better launch in my life. Went off without a hitch. Sometimes they stick, and we have no end of bother.—Now, admiral,' he went on, with a twinkle in his eye, 'shall we go to lunch, or would you prefer to walk round the yard?'

'Lunch!' nodded Sir Roger rather breathlessly. 'Lunch! And something cool to drink!'

'Roger! Behave yourself!' came another warning hiss.

So Kitty, with a last lingering look over her shoulder at the ship she had launched so truly, was dragged unwillingly away. Lunch was an everyday affair. Launching a ship was not.

And at lunch they had champagne and many speeches. They drank Kitty's health, the *Cyclone's* health, and the firm's health. And the senior member made a speech; Kitty replied rather haltingly; and the admiral, being a large shareholder and a bit of a celebrity, also spoke, mopping his brow with a brilliant bandana handkerchief as he did so. He caused Lady Trevelyan to squirm and his audience to rock with laughter at his rather nautical way of expressing himself; but what did that matter? They were all very happy together, and the luncheon was excellent.

After the meal the senior member of the firm requested Miss Katherine Trevelyan to accept the mallet and chisel as a memento of the occasion, and also a more personal gift in the shape of a brooch set with diamonds and sapphires that were just the colour of Katherine's eyes. It was quite a nice brooch —a most expensive one, though to the critical eye of Lady Trevelyan it was perfectly obvious that a man had chosen it. There was a certain solidity about it which was quite unmistakable.

And Katherine accepted the gifts very prettily. Indeed, she treasures them to this day, though she is Miss Trevelyan no longer; and a young Roger, named after his grandpapa, once did his best to sharpen his infant teeth upon the mallet, and was with considerable persuasion prevented from attempting the sword-swallowing trick with the glittering and most delectable chisel.

But even though she launched the ship nearly nineteen years ago, the lady still regards the *Cyclone* as her vessel; while those who serve on board the destroyer are proud to have her as their fairy-godmother. Woollen mufflers, sea-boot stockings, gramophone records, books, games for the officers—anything in reason they care to ask for—is always forthcoming. A fairy-godmother is the most useful relation one can possibly have, particularly if she happens to be a rich and generous woman.

III.

When first the *Cyclone* took the sea she was looked upon as one of the crack ships of the destroyer navy. Her builders were proud of her, for, having done 32.12 knots on her maiden trials on the measured mile, she was something of a flier. And a month or so after her completion, when she commissioned for service in a flotilla, her officers and ship's company cocked their chests and affected to pity the unfortunates who were condemned to serve in 'those rotten old twenty-seven knotters.' Moreover, since the *Cyclone* had a rather larger wardroom and a better skipper's cabin than any craft which had gone before, she was naturally selected by the 'commodore,' the courtesy title of the commander in charge of the flotilla, to serve as his flagship.

She was painted dead-black all over, and had a long, low hull, with three stumpy funnels, and a short mast forward. She carried a couple of torpedo-tubes, and one 12-pounder and five 6-pounder guns; while her deck was so littered with ventilating-cowls, engine-room casings, and other necessary paraphernalia that it was difficult to walk forward without barking one's shins. Her lines were very sharp, and her low bow was crowned with a curved turtle-back instead of the high, weatherly forecastle of her more modern successors. The little bridge, with the 12-pounder, the engine-room telegraphs, compass, and steering-wheel, was perched on the after-end of this turtle-back, some twenty-five feet abaft the stem, so that in anything like moderate weather, when her pointed forefoot drove through the seas rather than over them, she slopped the green water over the bows until it came surging aft to erupt against the canvas bridge-screens. She was always a bit of a pig in dirty weather; but bad weather in those piping times of peace did not very much matter. Destroyer captains who drove their ships unnecessarily were not popular with the powers that be when they retired to a dock-yard with bridges flattened, and deck fittings 'lost overboard in heavy weather.' So, if the glass went down with a thump, and the sea and the wind rose, it was generally advisable to turn tail and scuttle for shelter, or else to refrain from leaving harbour at all.

For over a year the *Cyclone* did duty as the senior officer's ship of the Portsmouth flotilla, during which period, though she did her fair share of running, life was not so very strenuous. The navy was in the betwixt and between stage in those days. A struggle with a first-class naval Power was regarded as only a vague possibility, and nobody really very much worried his head about it. Destroyers, moreover, were still comparative innovations, and were carefully nursed; while, in the whole of the British Isles, there were only twenty-four actually in commission, a flotilla of eight being attached to each of the home ports, Portsmouth, Devonport, and Chatham. All the others were kept in reserve in the dockyard basins, and, with many strange old battleships and cruisers, some of which were

still armed with muzzle-loading guns, were only commissioned and sent to sea once a year for the annual naval manœuvres.

The actual ten days or a fortnight during which the manœuvres lasted were pretty strenuous as things went, though, as the make-believe wars took place in the summer, when the weather was generally good, they were really rather enjoyable. Then it was that destroyer captains, always eager to show their mettle, satisfied their lust for excitement by dashing at full speed into 'hostile' harbours and torpedoing the opposing battleships, or else by landing men on the 'enemy's' coast to 'destroy' signal stations, and to pursue fat and overheated coast-guard men fleeing for safety with the secret codes and ciphers. Occasionally, to vary the monotony, they ran alongside their anchored rivals at dead of night, and 'cut them out' from under the guns of their own defences in the most approved naval style; while sometimes they had even the impudence to harry the military. Some of their varied encounters were most realistic.

But there were no wireless telegraphy, no submarines, and no seaplanes; there was no patrolling a turbulent North Sea or English Channel for days, weeks, and months, summer and winter alike, fair weather or foul, fogs, rain, gales, hail, or snow. Moreover, there were no German submarines to be strafed, or to strafe one with a torpedo when one least expected it. There were no minefields to be dodged or to be blundered upon in hazy weather. Naval war in 1900, even if it had come to pass, would have been a gentlemanly and straightforward occupation compared with what it is to-day.

When the manœuvres were not in progress the *Cyclone* and her flotilla would leave their home port for an occasional month's cruise, visiting harbours on the south coast and in the Channel Islands, and sometimes going farther afield to the Irish Sea or the west coast of Scotland. Whilst on these trips they carried out one or two 'night runs' a week to prevent the officers from losing the knack of station-keeping in close formation after dark; but on all the other nights of the week, and during the week-ends themselves, they were usually anchored in some convenient harbour where officers and men could have a chance of going ashore and enjoying themselves in their various ways. They also carried out practices with their guns and torpedoes, with an occasional night attack under war conditions upon a squadron of heavy ships at sea.

And when the cruises were over they would return to the Fountain Lake jetty in Portsmouth dockyard, when the married officers and men had leave to visit their families. So life, taking it all round, was extremely pleasant.

The *Cyclone*, as befitted the vessel carrying the commodore, was always spotlessly clean. Her ship's company, indeed, called her 'the yacht,' and woe betide the unfortunate stoker who appeared from a hatchway and left a trail of grimy footmarks on the beautiful brown corticene on the upper deck! He would be set to clear up the mess in his spare time by the 'first lieutenant,' otherwise 'the sub.,' who, as second in command, was the executive officer of the little ship. Destroyers carried only four officers in those days—the captain, either a commander or a senior lieutenant; a two-striped engineer officer, then known as an 'engineer,' but now as an 'engineer-lieutenant;' the ubiquitous sub., usually a young gentleman of about twenty-one with a flamboyant taste in handkerchiefs; and the gunner. The C.O., while he messed in the wardroom, had his own little cabin in the stern of the ship, but the other three officers lived, ate, and slept in the wardroom. The sleeping was the worst part of it, for sometimes one or other of the occupants snored.

The ship was always garbed in successive coats of dull black paint. Every little bit of woodwork that could be scrubbed was scrubbed, and all the rest was varnished. The copper ventilating-cowls, the sirens on the funnels, and the brasswork on guns, torpedo-tubes, wheel, and engine-room telegraphs shone and scintillated in the sun. It was the guns that were the *pièce de résistance.* Their barrels were coated with a special and evil-smelling browning compound, the exact ingredients of which were a mystery except to him who made it, but which produced a surface as hard and as glossy as that of a mirror. To keep them up to the mark they were polished daily with chamois leather and much elbow-grease, and were carefully swathed in little flannel jackets at night lest the precious coating should be scratched by the rude contact of the painted canvas covers.

The whaler and the dinghy, the only boats she carried besides a couple of collapsible Berthons, were a sight for the gods. They were black enamel outside and white enamel in, and had narrow lines of gold-leaf inside just below the gunwales, and fancy scarlet ribands outside under their well-scrubbed rubbing-streaks. Their oars and woodwork were always spotless, and they had polished brass yokes for steering, and sets of white cushions piped with blue for the stern-sheets.

There was no doubt about it: the *Cyclone* was a smart ship. But it was hard to understand how Bullivant, the sub., who hadn't a brass farthing beyond his pay of five shillings per diem, plus a shilling a day 'hard-lying money,' managed to do it. The sum spent on polishing-paste, varnish, Bath-brick, emery-powder, and shark's skin for scouring wood-work must have accounted for half his one hundred and nine pounds ten shillings a year. But Bullivant knew a thing or two, particularly with a dockyard under his lee.

After a year on home service, the *Cyclone* was sent to the Mediterranean, where, with white sides and yellow funnels, but with a new set of officers and men, she looked more like a yacht than ever. She was out there for seven years, and how many thousands of miles she steamed in that period, how many places she visited, I cannot say for certain. By the end of 1908, however, painted black once more, she was serving in one of the flotillas attached to the Home Fleet. She was still a good steamer, but was beginning to be looked upon as more or less of an old crock, for she and her sisters had long been superseded as the crack destroyers by the larger craft of the 'River class,' which, named after rivers in the British Isles, carried a more powerful armament, and had high forecastles instead of the low, old-fashioned turtle-backs. But even so, the *Cyclone's* young lieutenant and commander,* though secretly rather envious, affected to laugh at them. His ship, though elderly, could still do her twenty-nine knots in fine weather, whereas the 'Rivers' were built for no more than twenty-five and a half.

For eighteen strenuous months she remained in her new flotilla doing useful work, until, in the middle of 1910, by which time the 'River class' had themselves been superseded by craft of almost double their size, of considerably more speed, and much better armed, the poor old *Cyclone* found herself banished to a reserve flotilla at Portsmouth, or the 'Sinking Sixteenth,' as people jocularly and libellously called it.

She was now a 'nucloid,' the last stage of the elderly and the superannuated; and though her officers and men were brought up to full strength for the annual manœuvres, as would have been the case in the event of war,

* I must apologise for launching forth into a lengthy footnote, but this seems a fitting place for an explanation.

The specific rank of 'lieutenant-commander' for lieutenants of over eight years' seniority—that is, those who wore the two gold stripes and curl on their coat-sleeves, with the thin stripe between them—was not instituted until the early part of 1914. Prior to this the name of any lieutenant in the independent command of a ship was shown under his vessel's name in the Navy List, irrespective of his seniority, as 'lieutenant *and* commander.' But this was never a specific rank, and involved no change in uniform. It merely implied that the officer was in command of a ship.

At the present time a lieutenant in command of a vessel is shown in the Navy List under his ship's name as 'lieutenant in command;' but this again is not a rank.

It is as well to recollect that a lieutenant in the Royal Navy, who ranks with a captain in the army, always uses his title.

throughout the remainder of the year she carried no more than three-fifths of her proper complement. Her skipper was a young and newly married lieutenant, and the *Cyclone* was his first command; and though a gunner sometimes appeared on the scene for cruises, the engineer-lieutenant was the only other permanent officer in the ship.

The three-fifths crew were deemed to be sufficient for running her for exercise cruises, provided they were not too strenuous, and for keeping her tolerably clean and in good order. But more often than not her black side was streaked like the side of a zebra, while her brasswork was painted over or unpolished. Her outward appearance, in fact, had gone to the dogs. It was not because her commanding officer was not proud of her. On the contrary, from the way he talked, one would have imagined that he commanded a Dreadnought; while he himself, the ' chief,' and the whole of the ship's company were quite firm in their conviction that the *Cyclone* was still the best ship of her class.

But how could she be kept in her former state of cleanliness when the total upper-deck complement consisted of ten men, including petty officers ? Something had to go, so outward appearance did; and the ship, from a young and pretty girl with a pride in her own good looks, became a bedraggled and rather disreputable old harridan with a mottled complexion.

But, believe me, her efficiency did **not**

suffer. She still worked arduously for her living, and spent nearly as much time at sea as she did when in a 'running flotilla' attached to the Home Fleet. Things, indeed, were more strenuous than ever, for there were fewer men to do the work.

Twice a year, spring and autumn, she and her flotilla proceeded for six weeks to the west coast of Scotland, where they did exercises, ran their torpedoes, and fired their guns. Gunnery by this time had become the great god which ruled the entire navy, and woe betide even the old *Cyclone* if she did not succeed in hitting the target the requisite number of times! It assuredly meant a court of inquiry and a severe censure for some one or other if she did not, for good shooting was the one thing which counted.

And sometimes they sent her to the stretch of water in which she would have her being in time of war, until she developed a nodding acquaintance with every rock and sandbank, every buoy and landmark, every ripple, every tide-rip, each gray fog-bank, and each white-topped comber foaming in from the south-westward in her own particular domain.

And well it was that she knew these things, for in August 1914, by which time she had reached the very respectable age of fifteen, the purpose for which she had been built, the function for which pretty Miss Katherine Trevelyan had launched her, the great adventure for which she had prepared for so many years, actually came to pass.

The old ship might not be beautiful to look at. She might be downright old and ugly; but she felt quite young and skittish when the news reached her, and her very young skipper danced three times round the wardroom table.

The chief artificer-engineer, who by this time had relieved an engineer-lieutenant, was not quite so hysterical. He was an older and a much wiser man, 'a bundle man,* with a family, so he made his will on a half-sheet of notepaper, and got the newly joined gunner to witness it.

That the will has not yet been proved hardly matters.

* 'Bundle man,' a naval expression for a married man. I am not aware whether the wife and children constitute the 'bundle,' but the term probably originated from the little bundles wrapped in blue handkerchiefs which the married men in a home port generally used to take ashore with them.

Until quite recently the allowance of meat for each officer and man in the navy was one pound per day. In a large mess containing anything up to twenty men this amount was seldom consumed, and, provided he did not exercise the privilege too often, and did not land more than four pounds at any one time, a married man in a home port was allowed by the regulations to purchase the rest of his mess's meat at the contract rate, and to take it ashore for the use of his family. If there were several married men in a mess, they took it in turns. It was a considerable saving, for I can remember the days when the contract price of the best beef was fourpence a pound, and the growl of indignation which arose when it was raised to sixpence.

The same rule also held good as to the landing of other non-dutiable provisions, so that it was no rare thing in a ship in a home port to see numbers of men going ashore with their little bundles and parcels of provisions, which helped to feed their wives and children.

CHAPTER VI.

THE STORY OF THE 'CYCLONE'—WAR.

I.

'WHAT d'you make of her, sir?' asked the gunner, as his commanding officer put down his glasses.

'Blest if I know,' the captain grunted, still gazing at the small, midge-like object silhouetted against the pale primrose of the dawn. 'She's flying pretty low—'bout five thousand, I should think. Is the A.A. gun manned?'

'Yes, sir.'

'Right. You'd better go aft. I'll sing out if I want you to open fire. She may be one of our own, doing her morning patrol; but, coming from that direction'—he waved a hand to the eastward—'she might quite easily be a Boche. So keep your eyes skinned, gunner, and if I do sing out, mind you let her have it!'

'Ay, ay, sir.'

The burly Mr Vickery, looking more elephantine than ever in his thick muffler, hooded duffle coat, and huge leather sea-boots, clambered heavily down the steel ladder and made his way aft. Jonathan Cornelius Bundy, sometime chief officer of a White Star Liner, but now lieutenant-commander, R.N.R., and the *Cyclone's* captain, lit his pipe and resumed his tramp, the everlasting three steps forward, turn, three steps back, turn—all the exercise the tiny bridge gave him room for. He kept an ever-watchful eye on the distant speck in the sky, however, but was quite unperturbed. Seaplanes, even bomb-dropping Boches, were no strangers to him. The particular stretch of water patrolled by the *Cyclone* was far too close to a hostile coast for their advent on a fine day to be anything but an incident.

It was getting on for six o'clock in the morning—four bells in the morning watch, to be ultra-nautical—and the *Cyclone* was slipping along on her usual beat at an easy fifteen knots. There was hardly a ripple on the sea or a breath of wind in the air, nothing but the splash and gurgle of the bow wave, as she drove through the water, and the gentle fanning of the breeze caused by her movement.

To the westward, but still invisible in the early morning gloom, lay the English coast. In the opposite direction, to seaward, the star-spangled indigo of the heavens was gradually giving way to the ever-lightening hues of sunrise as daylight approached. The eastern sky gradually changed from cream to primrose, from this to a lurid chrome-yellow, and then to an opalescent riot of orange, copper, purple, and rose-pink, mingled with the purest of turquoise-blue and patches of the palest green, as the sun neared the horizon.

It was March, and bitterly cold. The month, as usual, had come in like a raging lion with a succession of gales, though this particular dawn, in so far as its actual weather went, might quite well have been filched from summer. But Bundy regarded the eastern sky with a sailor's ready suspicion. It was magnificent to look at, certainly; but the glass was unsteady, and he had every reason to know that a vivid sunrise with green and copper in the sky usually portended wind, and plenty of it. And wind meant a heavy sea, which, for the *Cyclone*, was always very unpleasant.

But there was something to be thankful for. At noon the ship would be relieved by her opposite number, and would return into harbour for her forty-eight hours' 'stand off,' when, if he were lucky, and too much paper-work had not accumulated in his absence, the skipper might go ashore for an hour or two to see his wife. He might also make up for arrears in the way of sleep.

The *Cyclone*, it must be understood, carried only two deck officers besides himself—a sub-lieutenant, R.N.R., and Mr Vickery, the gunner. These two generally kept watch on and watch off, the captain helping them out by keeping the two 'dogs'*—4 till 8 P.M.—and by sending them below whenever he could spare them from the bridge in the day-time. Nevertheless Bundy himself was the hardest-worked of the three. His subordinates could be tolerably certain of four hours' undisturbed sleep one night, and eight hours the next; but he never saw his bunk at all when the ship was at sea. He only went below for meals in the day-time, and spent his nights, when not actu-

* That is, dog-watches.

ally on the bridge, dozing in a deck-chair somewhere handy to it. The wireless was ever busy, and things were always happening. They were unimportant things as a rule; but the skipper was never really happy in his mind unless he were instantly available.

After all, their patrolling-ground was a bare fifty miles from a hostile coast, and fifty miles is an easy two hours' steaming for a marauding destroyer. Any dark night might see one of the enemy's favourite 'tip-and-run' dashes to sea, so at night the *Cyclone* was always ready for instant action with her guns and torpedo-tubes manned. Bundy did not wish himself and his ship's company to ascend to the heavens in a pyrotechnic display, nor did he relish the prospect of the *Cyclone's* perforated hull, or what remained of it, sinking noisily to a nameless grave at the bottom of the sea, to remain there in perpetuity, with no more glorious epitaph than 'Wreck, 1918,' on the Admiralty charts, and no more ornamental tombstone than the mystic symbol ‖* to mark her final resting-place. It seemed so anonymous and feeble a method of going under.

Of course, it was quite possible, even probable, if some big brute of a hostile destroyer did happen across her on a dark night, that his ship, with her inferior speed, her small guns, and her ancient torpedoes, might get it badly 'in the neck.' She might even be sunk; but nobody—least of all, the authorities—really

* The symbol ‖ is placed on a chart to mark the position of a wreck.

minded that, provided at least one Boche suffered a similar fate; and after all, as Bundy once observed, 'David did flop out Goliath, so we've always a chance.'

But the constant forty-eight hours in and forty-eight hours out on patrol, week in and week out, fair weather or foul, sometimes became deadly dull and monotonous. It was weary and enervating work to have to be waiting continually for something which never seemed to come; for, though other ships had fought with German destroyers, and had had the luck to sink hostile submarines, the *Cyclone* hadn't met either.

The watchers were ever at a disadvantage. The sea was always full of their own friends, and on sighting a dark, rushing shadow which might be an enemy, they had to make absolutely certain she was hostile before blazing away with their guns, firing their torpedoes, or dashing in with the oldest, but still the most potent and certain, weapon of all, the ram. They had always to be on the alert, and the strain on the personnel, particularly in bad weather and during the long nights of winter, was sometimes almost unbearable.

The enemy's destroyers suffered from no such anxiety. They, with their men perfectly fresh, could sally forth from their ports at their own selected moment, and, going 'all out,' could dash in among the patrols and use their guns and torpedoes to the fullest advantage with the absolute certainty that anything they sighted was British. Nobody who was not a

Waiting for something which never seemed to come.

PAGE 106.

fool could say that the hostile forays were not well planned and executed, or that the enemy were not dashing and brave; but their job was certainly the easier of the two. They could choose their own time. They were never at sea for prolonged periods, which made all the difference in the world.

The sun had risen, and the seaplane, approaching from astern, was barely three miles distant, and seemed gradually to be coming lower on a long, gentle glide. Bundy, however, still had the sun in his eyes, and could distinguish no identification marks on her wings; while, as most seaplanes have a strong family likeness, nobody was prepared to swear to her nationality. She might be friendly or she might be hostile; but, taking no chances, he had increased speed and was zigzagging in his course. He had been bombed before, and did not relish the experience.

They had not very long to wait. The machine was coming up hand over fist, and as the skipper again put up his glasses to look at her there came an eerie, whistling whining in the air. The sound increased in a screeching crescendo—then a splash, and a tall plume of spray glimmering golden in the strong light of the newly risen sun. The bomb dropped about five hundred yards distant in the *Cyclone's* wake, and almost at once the thudding, muffled crash of its explosion thundered out across the calm sea. The column of water toppled, to vanish in a little, circular, discoloured patch on the surface.

'Rotten!' Bundy muttered, dropping his glasses and picking up a megaphone. 'After-gun!' he shouted, waving an arm. 'Let go as soon as you like!'

The small six-pounder on her A.A. mounting in the stern was already pointing her lean muzzle in the air, and even as he spoke there came a spurt of flame, the sharp smack of exploding cordite, and a thin cloud of dun-coloured smoke. The shell went whistling skyward, while a man performed some sleight-of-hand with a lever, and the empty brass cylinder tinkled to the deck as the weapon recoiled and ran out again. The loading number pushed home another round, and the breech-block flew up with a metallic thud.

'Ready!' he bawled.

'That one went astern and above her, Maynard,' grunted the gunner as the shell burst in

H·R·J.

a tiny sparkle of flame and a little bulbous cloud of purplish smoke. 'Come down a thousand, and give her a bit less.—Oh lor! here's another!'

Wh-e-ee—EE—W! B-o-o-m-p! again. This time the splash of the missile leapt out of the water within a couple of hundred yards.

'Persistent brute!' murmured the captain on the bridge, as the coxswain, breathless and rather *décolleté*, arrived at the wheel. 'Hard aport, cox'n!'

'Hard aport it is, sir;' and the destroyer slithered round on her heel.

The six-pounder barked a second time, and this time the smoke-puff from the projectile seemed to dart out in the air close in front of the machine, now at a height of little more than three thousand feet.

'Crash!' went the gun again, but mingled with the roar of the report came that horrible screeching whistle as another bomb fell. The noise was far louder than before, and the bomb fell a bare thirty feet on the destroyer's port quarter. A shower of splinters went whistling overhead, while the stunning concussion seemed to lift the stern of the little ship bodily into the air, and to shake it like a rat in the jaws of a terrier. The sounds of rapidly disintegrating glass and china, jerked off the hooks and racks and hurled to the deck, floated up the hatch from the wardroom pantry.

'There goes our perishin' breakfast!' snorted

the gunner. 'Oh, you dirty hound!' he exclaimed an instant later, almost inarticulate with rage as the fountain of spray flung up by the explosion curled round in mid-air and came lashing down on deck to drench him and every member of the gun's crew. 'Knock it off, can't you?' He shook an impotent fist in the air. 'Come on, lads!' he continued to his men, shaking himself like a dog. 'Get another round off! We don't mind bein' bloomin' well 'alf-drowned, do we? We're bally well used to it by this time!'

Another shell flew off into space, and again the ball of smoke appeared very close to the target, so close that the novices among the small crowd craning their necks heavenwards held their breaths, and expected every moment to see a stricken Boche come hurtling down from the sky like a shot pigeon. But she merely swerved in her flight, and then started to move round to the left in a wide, sweeping circle, mounting as she went.

'Cease firing!' came an order from the bridge as the gun-muzzle followed her round.

'Cease firin'!' snorted an indignant stoker. 'What the 'ell's the skipper thinkin' abart? She's comin' round to drop some more of 'er ruddy heggs on us!'

'No, she ain't, Ginger,' contradicted another man. 'She's orf 'ome.'

''Ome be damned!' exclaimed Ginger. 'D'you think I 'aven't never seen one o' these 'ere things before?'

'I thinks she is, any'ow.'

'An' a ruddy fat lot you knows abart it! You 'aven't bin in th' navy more 'n six months, an' in this ship more 'n six weeks! Wot the 'ell d' you know abart it?'

The controversy went on, becoming more and more heated and personal as it continued. The aeroplane was quite forgotten.

The *Cyclone* meanwhile was humming along at over twenty knots, still twisting and turning, while her enemy completed her circling movement and made off in the direction whence she had come. She made no further effort to approach, and her pilot had evidently decided to go home, for his machine was still climbing on a long, upward slant. The destroyer, helm hard over, turned and scurried after her at top speed.

Then it was that those on deck realised the reason for their commanding officer's order to cease firing, for high overhead to the westward, coming towards them with the golden sheen of the risen sun shining on the underside of her wings, was another seaplane. She was a small, very fast machine, and had evidently been attracted to the spot by the sounds of gun-fire.

'Damn my wig and whiskers!' chuckled the blood-thirsty gunner, dropping his glasses to the full extent of their strap as he caught sight of the blue, white, and red circles on her wings. 'That's one of ours! She'll bloomin' well teach the other perisher to give us all a wet shirt, blast her!'

It was a very clear morning, and the pilot

of the British machine, a single-seater biplane,
had evidently spotted his enemy silhouetted
like a gnat against the glowing sunrise. He
was high above her, and in less than a minute
he had passed the *Cyclone* and was steering
on a bee-line to the eastward to cut off the
Boche's retreat. The latter, however, evidently
knew he was being chased, and was certainly
not wanting in bravery or determination. He
was probably aware that he would be over-
hauled, and would have to fight in any case ;
but before his pursuer arrived within a mile of
him he banked steeply round on one wing-tip
and started to climb in a wide spiral.

'Oh, cricky!' gasped Mr Vickery, open-
mouthed in astonishment as the British pilot,
seizing his opportunity, put the nose of his
machine down and dived at an alarming angle
straight towards his opponent.

The German, seeing the manœuvre,
abandoned his intention of climbing, and
flattened out in a straight flight to the north-
westward. But he was too late. The single-
seater, falling like a meteor, and swerving as
she dived, was on him before he could draw
another breath ; and mingled with the roaring
of the stokehold fans as the vessel pounded
along at full speed, those on the *Cyclone's* deck
could hear the frenzied stuttering of a machine-
gun opening fire. The British pilot was shooting into his opponent as he came down at an
angle of barely ten degrees from the vertical,
and in another second, after a rapid burst of
fire, he had crossed ahead of the Boche's

track, flattened out, and, passing underneath, zoomed up under her tail. Then, swinging round in a short circle, with his planes nearly vertical, he again approached his enemy from astern and slightly below her. The fiendish rattle of the machine-guns started afresh as the pair pumped bullets at each other.

It was quite impossible to follow every phase of the contest from the destroyer, for the two machines were never in the same relative position for two consecutive seconds. It was quite obvious, however, that the British seaplane was the speedier and handier machine of the two; but though she had this advantage, she was a single-seater scout, which meant that her pilot had to work his joy-stick with one hand whilst manipulating and firing his Lewis gun with the other. The German, a weightier machine, built for bomb-dropping, was slower and more unwieldy. She was a two-seater, however, so that the pilot could concentrate his attention on flying, while his observer did the fighting.

For two or three breathless minutes the pair circled like flies chasing each other round a gas-bracket, the stammering hiccup of their guns breaking out spasmodically as one or other of them gained a temporary advantage, and was able to pour in a burst of rapid fire. Sometimes they separated, only to come together again for another bout.

Purrrrt! Purr—rrt! chattered the guns. The British pilot was stunting all he knew —swooping, side-slipping, and banking, running through all his tricks as if he were giving an exhibition flight in an aerodrome. Once, after a dizzy swoop which brought a wave of apprehension surging to Bundy's heart, he did a complete loop backwards to maintain his position in rear of his enemy. His antics reminded one of the gambolling of a playful foal.

The German, too, evidently trying to shake him off, twisted and turned, dived and spun; but his slow, deliberate evolutions, dizzy though they would have appeared in ordinary circumstances, seemed, in comparison with those of his nimble enemy, like the lumbering movements of an elderly but rather skittish cart-horse. It was a nerve-racking performance to watch.

In the course of their frenzied tactics the two machines had come down to two thousand feet, while the *Cyclone* steamed round on the periphery of their aerial battle-ground, waiting for what might happen. Then, quite suddenly, the British machine toppled sideways on to one wing-tip, to fall an instant later into a sickening nose-dive.

'Oh, my God!' wailed Mr Vickery feebly, shaking all over as he watched her—'oh, my God!'

She seemed to be done for. Nothing short of a miracle could avert a hideous, headlong tumble into the sea, an awful impact which would smash pilot and machine alike into a shapeless pulp.

But the particular cherub who sits up aloft and watches over the interests of flight sub-lieutenants evidently had a very warm corner in his heart for this pilot, or else that particular young officer was endowed with more than the ordinary cunning, for the thing which seemed so utterly impossible actually came to pass. By some method best known to himself, he managed to recover control and to flatten out before reaching the water. His plane made a bad landing, it is true, hitting the water in a blinding upheaval of spray, and with a resounding crash which must have shivered her floats into mere matchwood, then fell drunkenly over on her side, with one wing limp and trailing in the water. She would fly no more. Her final disappearance was only a matter of minutes; but the catastrophe was not fatal, for as the destroyer steamed down to the rescue her men could see the pilot rise in his seat to extricate himself before the machine went under. They breathed again.

Every one was so intent upon watching him, in fact, that it was left for Mr Vickery's *bête noire*, the noisy, ordinary seaman, to raise an excited howl, and to point an agitated finger skywards.

'Look!' he shrilled, clutching his neighbour by the arm. 'Ow! Look at the other bloke; he's all smokin'!'

He was right. The Boche, with a stream of fire and a cloud of dense black vapour trailing out behind him, was coming down in a steep, spiral volplane. The pilot seemed still to have her under control, and was nerving every effort to reach the surface before the greedy flames devoured the thin fabric of his fuselage, rudders, and tail-planes, destroyed his stability, and hurled him whirling to the sea in a frightful dive which no human agency could possibly control.

There was dead silence on deck. Not a man cheered or uttered a sound, for it was far too awesome a spectacle for any popular outburst of feeling. Nobody likes to witness a fellow-creature being done horribly to death, even though he may be an enemy, and there was not a member of the *Cyclone's* ship's company who did not feel his generosity uppermost and hope that the seaplane would make a successful landing. They quite forgot that the pilot of that very machine had done his best to blow them out of the water with his bombs not so very long before.

But it was not to be. A wing suddenly collapsed, and the spiral volplane became a dive, in which the machine, dropping like a plummet, started to spin dizzily round and round, hopelessly out of control. And the end came in the drawing of a breath. She hit the water nose first at a ghastly speed, and with a thud which could almost be felt. There was a heavy splash, in the midst of which she seemed to crumble away and vanish. Indeed, all that was left when the *Cyclone* visited the spot shortly afterwards was a circle of blackened, oily water scattered all over with charred débris, the splintered remains of one huge, iron-crossed wing, which they salved as a memento, and the curling trail of slowly dissolving smoke athwart the heavens, with a thicker pall mingled with a few eddies of steam over the place where she had disappeared. There was no trace of any survivor, nothing but a vacuum flask nodding absurdly in the ripples, and a single fur gauntlet.

It was the work of a few minutes for the destroyer to run alongside the remains of the rapidly sinking British machine and to rescue the pilot, a little flight sub-lieutenant of the R.N.A.S. of barely more than twenty.

'Are you hurt, sir?' asked Mr Vickery anxiously, as they came within earshot, to find the surprising youth sitting calmly on the top plane, with his feet dangling in the water.

'No-o. I'm fairly all right, thanks,' the sub. said airily. 'If you'll send me down a line, we'll salve the old gun; it would be a pity to lose her. Hurry up, though. I can feel the old bus sinking.'

They dragged the weapon on board, with the pilot after it.

'Thank the Lord!' he said, standing on deck with chattering teeth. 'Deuced cold work sitting there with nothing to do. I'm sorry to see the last of her, though,' he added regretfully, looking over the side to where his seaplane was slowly going under. 'She's been a good old bus.'

'Are you hurt, sir?' inquired the gunner again, noticing that the boy was swaying ominously, and that his face was ghastly pale.

'My back-teeth are a bit loose,' the youngster confessed with an apology for a smile. 'We came down such a devil of a bump. That brute of a Hun shot away most of my engine and controls. I seem to have had one or two narrow squeaks myself,' he added, glancing down at various punctures in his yellow leather jacket. 'Flamin' bullets, some of 'em. They play perfect hell inside if they get you.' He pointed out two charred holes. 'M'yes, I thought so,' he went on, waggling his left arm. 'I've taken one through the shoulder. Thought I could feel the gore drippin' down my arm, but wasn't quite sure. Nothing to worry about, though. Pity we couldn't pick up the other Johnny. He put up'—— He suddenly clenched his teeth with pain. 'He put up a devilish good scrap.'

'Like a drop o' brandy, sir?' queried the gunner. 'You look mortal bad.'

'No good, I'm afraid. Thanks, all—— Lord!' he broke off suddenly, 'I do believe I'm going to faint.'

There were many willing arms to help him, but faint he did.

So they carried him below; and soon afterwards, when the *Cyclone* returned into harbour, the flight sub-lieutenant, still under the influence of morphia, lay wrapped in blankets in the skipper's bunk.

A 'thirty knotter' carries no medical officer, but, between them, the sub-lieutenant, R.N.R., and Mr Vickery had done the best they could for their patient, though a broken collar-bone, a bullet-wound in the shoulder, and another through the thigh were rather beyond their rude surgical knowledge.

But in spite of their rough-and-ready treatment, the flight sub-lieutenant is still alive. Nay, he is even alive and kicking.

II.

The fog which had come as they neared the land was so utterly thick and impenetrable that the horizon was a bare eighty yards distant. Even the motionless figure of the look-out man, perched on the stem-head twenty feet away, was blurred and indistinct in the steamy haze shrouding the sea; while beyond him, the dark horizontal shadows of the little ripples faded away into a gray luminous haze in which all sense of distance was lost. Endeavouring to probe its depths was as unsatisfactory as gazing at a pane of frosted glass to see what lay behind it.

. 'I put her here, sir,' said the sub., pointing with the end of his dividers at a pencil-mark on the chart laid out on the table before him. 'If we run on another twelve minutes we might make this buoy. If we don't, our dead reckoning puts us there, and we should alter course to north fifty-four east.'

Bundy, lowering his eyes from their scrutiny of the murk over the bows, glanced at the printed sheet with its pencil-line showing the ship's track.

'We sha'n't sight the buoy unless we hit it end on,' he grunted. 'What about tide?'

'I've allowed three-quarters of a knot to the nor'-westward, sir.'

'Deviation?'

'One and a half degrees east, sir.'

'Um; that's about right. But I'm none too certain of it.* It's been all over the shop since we came out of dock, and we can't afford to steer too much to port. There's this little lot.' He pointed to an area shaded in on the chart in a hectic scarlet.

Red ink on a chart is ever a warning of danger. In war-time it generally means mine-fields, and even British mines have not the sense to differentiate between friend and foe. They explode impartially on impact with any one foolish enough to run into them.

'That's where the *Typhoon* got it in the neck last Friday,' continued the skipper. 'D'you remember her being towed in stern first?'

'Do I not?' said the sub., scratching his beardless chin. 'But Friday's always an unlucky day.'

'Any day's unlucky if your luck's out. D'you think we could afford to steer a couple o' degrees more to starboard?'

The sub. shook his head. 'Shouldn't advise it,' he said. 'There's this bunch of trouble.

* Deviation is the error induced in the compass by the mag-netism of the ship. It is a variable quantity, and has to be checked by frequent observation, more particularly as it changes for every direction of the ship's head, and has to be allowed for when courses are shaped by compass.

It's just as bad as the mines to get mixed up with.'

'All right,' the captain agreed. 'We'll let her rip and trust to luck. But I wish I was more certain about the deviation. And the tides are the very devil hereabouts.'

The *Cyclone* was in no very pleasant locality. She was groping her way down a narrow stretch of water between a scarlet minefield on the one hand, and an area marked on the chart in blue on the other. The azure portion represented a section of sea containing certain diabolical and very potent contrivances for the special discomfiture of hostile submarines. The only consolation was that the British craft knew whereabouts the dangerous areas were, while Fritz did not.

And Bundy, good seaman though he was, felt vaguely anxious. It was really his 'day off' in harbour, but as the *Cyclone* was the only ship available, she had been sent to sea on certain urgent business which brooked no delay, and had to be carried through at all costs. Within half-an-hour of her sailing the fog had shut down as thick as any blanket. The tide, as he had pointed out, was erratic, while on occasion the *Cyclone's* standard compass became possessed of a magnetic little devil which no man could properly exorcise. There was a minefield to port, an equally unhealthy area to starboard, innumerable sandbanks and shoals farther ahead if they escaped the other dangers, and a Jonah in the wardroom in the shape of a red-tabbed, beribboned brigadier-general of His Majesty's Army. What more could one desire?

The brigadier, in fact, was the 'urgent business,' and was a very special sort of Staff-officer returning to the scene of his activities in France after a hurried conference in London. But he had disappointed the *Cyclone's* ship's company sadly, for he was not the least bit like an ogre. They had expected to see a red-faced, fiercely-moustached, and fiery-tempered person with a voice like rolling thunder and an eye like a basilisk's. Not a bit of it. The brigadier was about the same age as Bundy, with a merry blue eye and a pleasant smile, and had made himself extremely affable to everybody. Indeed, he had even apologised profusely for giving the ship a trip to sea on her 'day off;' and now, oblivious of the fog, and entertained by Mr Vickery, he was making a belated but very substantial breakfast in the wardroom.

But the skipper could not help feeling rather nervous at having him on board, for brigadiers on the Staff were rather more valuable than the average run of people. Moreover, he was in fear and trembling lest the passenger should appear on the bridge and start asking questions. Some questions are very awkward, especially if the weather is thick and the position of the ship is more or less a matter of conjecture and uncertainty.

Bundy, indeed, felt that the whole reputation of the British Navy rested on his shoulders.

It would never do for a soldier—a very distinguished soldier, judging from the kaleidoscopic array of ribbons on his bosom—to be blown up on a mine, or to leave the ship with an idea that undistinguished sailormen were in the habit of losing themselves in fogs. They never did such things in the army. So Mr Vickery, the only available host, had been given precise and very explicit instructions that the brigadier was to be kept below over his meal for just as long as it could possibly be spun out. But even a hungry soldier cannot linger over breakfast for ever.

'Hell!' suddenly muttered the lieutenant-commander, glancing aft to see the khaki figure of his passenger, shepherded by the gunner, advancing warily along the narrow deck. 'He's coming up here!'

'Oh lor!' said the sub. 'That's torn it! Suppose he asks where we are?'

'Smile sweetly and just plump your finger on the chart and say, "This is the exact spot, sir." No humming and hawing, mind; and don't hesitate. Don't, for the Lord's sake, tell him we're anywhere near a minefield! He mightn't like it.'

'Do you mind my coming on the bridge?' asked the brigadier, halting at the foot of the ladder.

'Not a bit, sir,' said Bundy, with a cordiality he didn't really feel. 'Let me give you a hand, sir. Be careful of your spurs.'

'I don't like these steep ladders of yours,' laughed the military officer, arriving rather breathless at the top. 'It beats me how you fellows manage to get up and down when it's rough.'

'Oh, we get used to it in time, sir.'

'Thank Heaven it's calm to-day! This fog's bad, though. Do you often get it?'

'Not really often, sir,' said Bundy, groaning inwardly at the thought of what his next question might be. 'I hope they gave you a good breakfast, sir,' he added, adroitly changing the subject.

'Best breakfast I've had for months, thanks to you. Very kind of you to take pity on me. I started from London at six this morning on nothing but a cup of tea. Tell me,' he continued, 'who is that stout officer who looked after me so well? I didn't quite catch his name.'

'That's Mr Vickery, the gunner, sir,' Bundy explained.

'Most entertaining man. Some of the stories he told me of your doings quite made my blood run cold.'

The captain could quite well believe it, for Mr Vickery was a born raconteur. 'I expect he piled it on a bit, sir,' he said. 'He's a holy terror for spinning yarns when he once gets started.'

The soldier smiled. 'What time d'you expect to put me ashore, by the way?'

'In about an hour from now, sir.'

'Shall I be in the way if I stay up here and look on? Say the word, you know, and I'll clear out.'

Really, he was quite the most accommodating 'brass hat' that Bundy had ever met.

'Stay, by all means, sir,' he said politely. 'I shall be de '——

'Something on the port bow, sir!' howled the look-out man in the bows, galvanised into sudden activity.

The commanding officer leapt to the fore side of the bridge, to see a vague, blurred-looking object looming up through the mist broad on the port bow. It was a bare eighty yards distant. It might be the buoy. But who ever saw a buoy like that? It was much too big.

The ship was travelling at eighteen knots, and in the drawing of a couple of breaths the thing was level with the bows. It was disappearing fast beneath the surface in a swirl of whitened water. It was an elongated gray mass, with hand-rails along its upper surface and a couple of upstanding things like spars. It had indistinct white figures on it. Bundy, trembling with excitement and his heart thumping like a sledge-hammer, knew!

In the brief moment vouchsafed to him in which to act he never lost his head. His mind worked quite clearly, and almost instantaneously he checked the first natural impulse to give the *Cyclone* full starboard helm in an effort to get home by ramming. Had he done so the final result might have been very different, for the submarine was well inside the destroyer's turning circle, and the *Cyclone* would never have swung round in time to deliver the blow.

Instead of that he did the very opposite, and shouting, 'Hard aport!' to the astonished quartermaster, who luckily had the presence of mind to obey the order without hesitation, swung the stern of his little ship towards the spot where the enemy was fast disappearing.

In another moment she had vanished; but the captain, bending down, had his hands on something on the floor of the bridge. He craned his neck to keep his eyes fixed on that whitened patch in the water. . . . He waited breathlessly. The *Cyclone's* stern was slewing fast.

'Good old girl!' he murmured beneath his breath. He pulled something hard, waited a moment, and pulled again.

He stood up with the sweat pouring off his face as the ship continued to swing. He darted round to the opposite side of the bridge to keep the spot under observation, jostling the astonished brigadier most rudely as he did so.

'Lord!' he murmured wildly. 'Don't say they're duds!'

They weren't. Hardly were the words out of his mouth when there came the muffled, thudding roar of an underwater explosion. The ship danced and trembled as if she had struck a rock, and some distance away on the starboard quarter a huge mushroom-shaped dome of snowy water came to the surface and broke like a bursting bubble into a sparkling column of upflung spray. Another deep concussion, and then the scene beggared description. The sea seemed literally to burst asunder with a rumbling crash like the eruption of a volcano. Then came a whistling roar like the sound of escaping steam, and a great fan-shaped mass of grayish-white water, stained with streaks of some denser, brownish liquid, went spouting skywards. And in the midst of the awful waterspout they saw the bodies of men, their arms and legs flung out at impossible angles, revolving grotesquely through the air; fragments of splintered wreckage and débris whirled round and round, up and down, like leaves in an autumn gale.

The submarine had been blown in two, divided like an egg, and the air from her interior, rushing to the surface, had carried in its stupendous blast every loose fitting and nearly every man.

It was a ghastly spectacle, and Bundy, sick at heart, felt his knees trembling beneath him. Even the brigadier, seasoned warrior though he was, seemed appalled, for his face was white under its tan as he clutched the bridge-rail and gazed at the eruption.

Then the scene became suddenly blotted out in a mist of spray as the torrent fell, pattering down on the water with a hiss like heavy rain. The air was filled with the pungent reek of oil-fuel. Great oily waves came rippling across the surface, and heavy, ominous splashes told of bodies and débris falling into the sea.

The *Cyclone* stopped her engines and went astern to check her way, and the atmosphere started to clear; but when they could see again there was nothing but a huge circular patch of oil-fuel floating in a thick black scum on the surface, with here and there fragments of wood and a life-belt or two. And there also were the remains of what, thirty seconds before, had been hale and hearty men. Their faces were bleeding, their bodies broken, mangled, and torn. They cried piteously for help—help which so often they themselves had denied to their victims.

'Oh—a-a-a-h!' came their drawn-out howls of agony. 'Ah—a-a-a-a-a-h!'

An arm waved hopelessly in the air, and then disappeared slowly beneath the surface. A boat had been lowered from the *Cyclone* to save life. She was in the water in record time, her crew pulling lustily towards the spot on their errand of mercy as if they were rescuing their own countrymen. But one by one the poor fellows sank, and their agonised crying was for ever stilled. At last only one was left. He floated motionless, making no effort to save himself, and him the *Cyclone's* whaler rescued. He was an officer, the U-boat's commander, and still breathed when they brought him on board and laid him out on the steel deck. But the flickering spark of life in the battered body was nearly extinct, and he died a minute later without even opening his eyes.

It was all over.

Less than an hour afterwards a very chastened-looking little destroyer crept apologetically alongside a jetty in a certain French port.

'Report why you are so late in arriving,' signalled the senior naval officer.

'Submit,' the *Cyclone* replied, 'we were delayed through stopping to sink a hostile submarine. Request an officer may be sent to examine evidence.'

So some one, rather annoyed at being dragged away from his work in the middle of a busy forenoon, came on board, admitted the truth of Bundy's claim, congratulated him heartily, and then ordered him unsympathetically to sea to resume his patrol.

And Bundy now wears on his breast a small strip of crimson ribbon edged with blue; while a U-boat's red-and-white life-buoy hangs in the hall of the brigadier-general's home somewhere in peaceful Surrey. As for the *Cyclone*, she becomes older every day, while her gray paint becomes dingier and her sides more and more dented and streaked and patched with rust. But she has fulfilled the purpose for which she was created, and, ancient hound though she may be, can still wag her tail with the best of her modern sisters.

CHAPTER VII.

OUR RIVER AND SOME DOGS.

I.

I AM tolerably certain that there is no other river in the British Isles quite like ours, the one in which, at the time of writing, the *Triptolemus* is lying at her buoy. It is a utilitarian, tidal waterway, alive with bustling traffic; a river in which Nature has been coerced into playing second fiddle to the needs of humanity. It is on such rivers as ours that man builds his wharves, his jetties, and his docks; erects his granaries and his warehouses, his shipbuilding yards, with their gaunt cranes and spidery gantries, and tall chimneys defiling the purity of the heavens with their abominable reek. The works of man in this direction are seldom beautiful. In our case they are, frankly, hideous.

And now, though no small portion of the traffic of commerce has given way to that of war, the ships still come and go on every tide. There are bluff-bowed freighters fresh from braving Fritz at sea—or off to brave him again—painted like futurist pictures in their camouflage—patches, squares, oblongs, circles, and stripes of black, blue, brown, gray, green, yellow, white, nearly every colour and shade under the sun except scarlet. Next are seen steam trawlers and drifters in their dozens, high-bowed, sturdy craft, with their spray-whitened funnels, newly arrived from mine-sweeping or the patrol-grounds in the fastnesses of the wild North Sea, each manned by her little company of North Sea fishermen—splendid fellows, as sturdy and as weather-beaten as their craft. They have many tales to tell, have these patrol-craft and mine-sweepers; and the tattered, smoke-

grimed ensigns fluttering bravely at their mizzens, and their business-like little guns, show that they hunt something rather more dangerous than fish. Then there come fussy, gray-painted motor-launches, very much the men-of-war with their mast-head pendants and general 'mind-my-paint' sort of aspect, manned by officers and men of the R.N.V.R., rabid enthusiasts, many of whom hardly thought of the sea before '14, much less of hunting real live submarines.

In case you have never seen an 'M.L.,' imagine a slim, motor-driven craft built of wood, and between sixty and seventy feet long. She carries a considerable amount of top-hamper for her size, a tiny dinghy, an absurd little mast, and provides accommodation for a couple of officers and three or four men, with their little gun, and sundry other potent contrivances for the annoyance of the wily Hun. And it was not so very long ago, on a foggy day in the Channel, that such a craft as this happened upon a submarine basking on the surface. Now, Fritz had two 4·1's, and the M.L. a three-pounder or so, but, nothing daunted, the latter opened fire and made at full speed for her huge opponent with the intention of ramming. Possibly it did not occur to the M.L.'s skipper that if his blow did get home the fragile hull of his craft would be splintered to mere matchwood. He simply went for the submarine bald-headed, and Fritz, not liking the look of affairs, slapped down his conning-tower lid and dived.

The M.L., however, on passing over the spot, dropped something from her stern which exploded under water and brought the submarine floundering to the surface like a stricken whale. She lay over on her side with her conning-tower nearly horizontal, and one propeller beating the water as she tried to submerge, while the M.L., drawing in, peppered her at close quarters. Every shot drove home and burst, but in the excitement of the moment the pigmy got too close, for presently the submarine's bow lifted out of the water with the motor-launch balanced upon it. The plucky little vessel slid off again with the loss of her rudder and both propellers, and, naturally enough, with her flimsy wooden bottom leaking like a colander. Her motive-power was gone, she was miles from home, and was sinking; but still she let drive with her little gun until Fritz gave up the ghost and went under for the last time in a mass of oil and bubbles. It was only by the mercy of Providence that the M.L. did not share her fate; but by dint of superhuman efforts her men kept their crazy craft afloat, and, with a couple of oars, and their blankets and bath-towels rigged as sails to the favouring breeze, succeeded in staggering back into harbour. Stout fellows!

And last, but not least, in our river are the destroyers. Their name is legion, and a truly representative gathering they are, belonging as they do to every imaginable type and class, from the three-hundred-and-fifty-ton 'thirty knotters' of 1897 to the vessels of twenty-one years later nearly four times their size. They come in for a while to rest after their activities at sea. They are here to-day and gone to-morrow, and their hair-raising adventures would fill many books. There are craft which have been in action in the Heligoland Bight, at the engagement on the

Dogger Bank in January 1915, at Jutland, and
off the Belgian coast; others which dashed
in, in broad daylight, to attack with their
antiquated torpedoes the enemy battle-cruiser
that bombarded the Hartlepools way back in
1914; several which have been provided with
new bows and sterns after altercations with
mines; and still more who can spin blood-
thirsty yarns of battles, successful and otherwise, with submarines. It was here, indeed,
that I renewed my acquaintance with the
Cyclone, though that is not her real name.
I served in that ship myself many years ago,
and still take an interest in her and a pride in
her doings. And let me say in passing that her
story in the last chapter is not mere fiction.

Our river is very wide; but only here and
there in its length are there towns, docks,
shipbuilding yards, and fish-markets. For the
most part its shores are low and flat, with no
hills in the background to break the horizon
beyond, so that even solitary buildings and
insignificant clumps of trees are silhouetted
against the skyline as objects of some importance. At low-water the banks are fringed
with mud-flats, acres and acres of shining,
viscous ooze, in which only the gulls and the
curlew can find a precarious resting-place.
Even the navigable channel in the centre of
the river is out of all proportion to its width,
and winds its tortuous way seaward between
many shoals and mud-banks.

The water, particularly on the ebb and after
heavy rain, when the soil is washed off the

uplands and is carried down-stream in the form of silt to make more mud-banks, is the colour and consistency of *café-au-lait*. So opaque is it, indeed, that when a ship passes up against the falling tide, her very bow wave and stern wash are drab-coloured instead of white; while, after scrubbing decks in the mornings—for we still go through the motions of trying to be clean—we invariably find a substantial portion of our native land, in the form of a fine, powdery deposit, adhering to the corticene when the heat of the sun has evaporated the moisture.

The tide runs six knots at 'springs' and about four at ordinary times. The only other river I can compare it with, indeed, is the Yang-tse-kiang, where the current is so swift and the silt so heavy that the river gunboats, when staying at a place for any length of time, have to lift their anchors off the bottom every morning. Otherwise, when the time for departure came, they would be so deeply buried that no capstan-engine would ever break them out of their muddy bed.

Our motor-boat travels six knots at full speed, so that sending ashore is something of an adventure, and generally we pin our faith to the 'trot boat.' You might imagine, from her title, that the trot boat is a smart-looking craft with a good turn of speed; but don't believe it. A 'trot' is a tier of buoys occupied by destroyers and other small vessels, and the trot boat is merely the steam-launch which acts as a ferry between us and the shore, and lands our liberty - men, recreation - parties, stewards, and postman, and brings them off again, together with our provisions and mails. We couldn't undertake the work ourselves in a place like this, for when at our buoy we are nearly a mile from the landing-place, and only at slack-water are our motor and pulling boats the least use.

The trot boat is not a beautiful object. She is fat and sturdy, carries a generous deck cargo of coal, and badly needs a scrub and a lick of paint. At full speed she pants like an asthmatic cart-horse; but she can just stem the tide, though sometimes, when it is against her, it takes a full hour or more to traverse the distance from ship to shore, and *vice versâ*. Occasionally, like all things human, she plays us false and doesn't appear at all, with the consequence that we are marooned on board, and don't get our mails and fresh provisions until late in the afternoon. She has always an excellent excuse for her non-appearance: (1) she is coaling, and will be ready in ten minutes; (2) she is taking in boiler water, and will be ready in half-an-hour; (3) she has had a break-down, and will be ready to-morrow; (4) she is inside the basin, and cannot get out because the lock-gates are shut; (5) the weather is too bad; and so on.

The bad weather excuse, I am forced to admit, is generally justified, for, when it does blow in this place, it blows with a vengeance, and not infrequently I have seen the trot boat staggering off with the drab-coloured spray flying in sheets over her funnel as her stub bow butted and splashed into the waves.

She is manned by trawler-men who have already done their fair share at sea during the war in mine-sweepers and patrol-craft. One member of the crew has even been blown up thrice, and he refers to these distressing episodes as the first, second, and third occasions on which 'them Admiralty Lords forks me out a new kit'! One could almost fancy, from the way he talks, that Sir Eric Geddes himself handed the garments in question over the counter of a gentlemen's ready-to-wear outfitting department somewhere in Whitehall.

On the last occasion on which this old veteran was blown up somebody tried to do him in the eye over a pair of new boots. He had his old ones on his feet when he was rescued, which was only natural.

'We was sweepin' along quite peaceful,' he said, 'when all of a sudden we run atop of a mine, an' the ship seems to break in 'alves afore I knows what's up. An' when I cooms to, I finds meself in the watter wi' some one a-pullin' me into a boat by me 'air.' He removed his cap at this stage, to exhibit the adornment in question. There wasn't much of it, and his pink scalp showed through the iron-gray bristles like sunlight between the tree-trunks in a fir plantation. 'It isn't ower plentiful, as you see,' he continued, laughing, 'but they pulls me out some'ow. But the worst of it was, I didn't 'ave no chance to take off me boots afore I was blawed up, you see. And when I goes up to get me noo kit, they sez to me '——

But it is a long story, and his remarks on the subject won't altogether bear repetition. He got his new boots, though.

Anyhow, this old gentleman—for he was well over military age—is a grandfather, as well as a fisherman. He has two sons fighting in France, while another was killed in Mesopotamia, and he himself wears the blue-and-white ribbon of the Distinguished Service Medal on the breast of his Sunday jacket. He was sent to the trot boat for a rest cure, but as he works twenty-four hours on and twenty-four hours off, and during the 'on' period lives in the boat and spends no small portion of his time in a state of partial saturation, I fail to see where either the rest or the cure comes in. However, he and his mates seem to thrive on it. They are always cheery, and eager to do their best for us, so we are sincerely grateful. We couldn't get on without the trot boat and the gang of rather unshaven pirates who man her, and an occasional polite suggestion, ' I s'pose you haven't got a bit o' 'bacca to spare ? ' never needs repetition.

It is evening now, and with the sun setting slowly in the west behind a bank of mist-wreathed, smoky purple, overtopped by a broad band of the most vivid crimson, merging higher up into rose-pink, then russet, citron, the palest turquoise, and finally a wonderful, deep sapphire, the river looks really beautiful.

But it is only a transient beauty, for to-morrow again it will be drab and gray, and from the look of the sky, I shouldn't at all wonder if it blew a gale before morning. Moreover, I am ever reminded by my olfactory sense that Nature is spoiled by the handiwork of man.

There is an aroma wafted towards us on the evening breeze. It is not the pleasing scent of new-mown hay, nor yet the fresh, indefinable smell of newly-turned earth. No. The odour —I am too polite to call it a ghastly stench— emanates from a dismal red-brick building on the shore directly in the wind's eye, a building which has three lean chimneys that vomit forth their black smoke perpetually. It is marked on the chart as ' Fish Manure Works,' and I can quite believe it. The smell of them is, frankly, terrific. The stink thereof ascendeth to the heavens. Need I dwell further upon the joys of it ?

And on the other side of us, almost within a stone's-throw, is a float to which is attached a large bell that tolls incessantly as the ripples sway it from side to side. I like the sound of bells mellowed by the distance, but this one has a monotonous, irritating clang which gets on my nerves. It reminds me of a funeral, and, like its prototype on the Inch-cape Rock, was put there ostensibly to prevent foolhardy mariners like myself from looking for trouble on the shoal patch in the centre of the fairway. I cannot compose my thoughts and collect my scattered wits—on paper, at any rate—with that maddening clang, clang . . .

tinkle, clankety, clang . . . sounding for ever in my ears. I can sympathise with Sir Ralph the Rover, and shall probably emulate him on the first convenient moonless night.

But what right have I to grumble, and who can expect peace and quietness aboard a ship of any kind, let alone a destroyer? The steel deck over my cabin is twelve inches above my head when I stand up, and the most ordinary footfall, as I think I observed before, sounds like a pair of giraffes dancing the tarantella. It isn't the fault of those who pass overhead. If they wish to pass from aft forward, or from forward aft, they must walk over my head. There is positively no alternative unless they take wings unto themselves and fly—which God forbid!

A destroyer is so absurdly thin that sound travels in a most unaccountable way. The sub. lives in a cabin in the flat next before mine, and when he strops his patent razor it sounds like some one giving a tympani solo. With practice, I believe I could even hear the chief E.R.A. blowing his nose in the engine-room; while at this moment, sitting at my writing-table, I can listen to the gramophone in the wardroom, which is two bulkheads away in the compartment abaft mine, rasping out 'Another Little Drink' from the *Bing Boys*, at the top of its rather raucous voice. Mingled with the infernal cachinnation of the bell—for I am convinced that the diabolical thing is laughing at me—the words of the song will persist in running through my head.

But even a gramophone has its uses. It can cheer people up; and I shall always remember the story—I believe, by the way, it has been immortalised by Rudyard Kipling—of the British submarine not so very far from Heligoland. She had made herself distinctly obnoxious by blowing a large German destroyer neatly in halves with a torpedo, and, having accomplished it, sank to the sea-bottom and lay doggo. But a prowling Zepp had witnessed the performance, and had summoned the hunters to the scene, and for some time those in the underwater craft listened to the roaring and whirring of propellers as they steamed to and fro overhead. Then came a short silence, followed by the ominous sound of scraping and tapping, as a chain or wire sweep, towed by some inquisitive Hun on the surface, was dragged over the submarine's hull. Secured to that sweep there must have been several explosive charges, and well the submarine's skipper knew it. If the chain caught in any projection in the hull, the simple pressure of a firing-key up topsides and—the subsequent proceedings would interest them no more.

It was a nasty noise, a nerve-racking noise, and to deaden the sound, and to quell the throbbing of his own anxious heart, the skipper switched on the gramophone. And when the tune was finished the eerie scraping had ceased and was no more heard. But the tune they played, I am informed on the very best authority, was 'Stop your tickling, Jock!'

Wouldn't Harry Lauder be pleased? But —well, you can never believe quite all the yarns these submarine folk tell you. They are nearly as bad as the destroyers!

II.

Dick, the Sealyham, who is living on board for the present, is possessed of a devil. Yesterday we gave him a bath, and this morning, looking like a fluffy little snowball, he left the ship under escort at half-past ten for his customary morning constitutional. He should have returned within the hour, but did not reappear until half-past twelve.

I do not so much object to his being absent over leave; neither can I complain when, in rainy weather, he comes back with his underneath portion covered in mud. His total freeboard amidships, which I have just measured, is exactly eleven and a half inches, so one can hardly expect anything else. But I had to put my foot down when he returned dark gray in colour, camouflaged all over with stars and stripes of oily black, his beard dripping in slime, and with a sweet smile on his cherubic countenance. He hadn't even the good manners to be ashamed of himself, and was so pleased when he returned that he wanted to share his slime with me.

It was the fault of the cat at the Y.M.C.A., and was due also to the fact that the floor of the hut is raised a few inches off the ground, a very necessary precaution, seeing that in inclement weather it lies in a sea of oleaginous, black mud.

'Who said "Huns"?'

H·R·J·

PAGE 142.

Whether or not the cat ogled Dick, or Dick made the first advances to the cat, I am unable to discover; but his custodian informs me that they played hide-and-seek together for a full hour and a half, in and out of the slime and the litter underneath the hut. He—the custodian—assures me, moreover, that he whistled and whistled till he was blue in the face and gasping for breath, but that they took no notice whatever. It was not until both sides had exhausted their energy that the game ceased. I must add, in passing, that I have heard that there is rather a pretty girl at the Y.M.C.A. Hence the direction of the walk.

But Dick is ever a contrary little animal, with a very decided will of his own and a peremptory manner. When he condescends to sleep peacefully in my arm-chair he is a perfect angel; but at intervals he wakes up with a start, cocks one ear, descends from the chair, and darts to the foot of the ladder leading to the upper deck, where, prancing like an impatient Dervish, he informs me loudly and insistently that there's a cat somewhere on deck which he needs must go and strafe. It isn't a cat at all, merely the wind flipping the hanging end of a rope from side to side; but when Dick asks for a thing, it is as well, for one's peace of mind, not to refuse him. He is so absurdly abbreviated in the legs, however, that he cannot negotiate the steep ladder by himself, and I have to help him.

Having done so, I am at liberty to resume my interrupted writing, while he looks for the cat, but finds her not. Next he realises that it is cold on deck, and getting bored, and fancying my arm-chair in front of the warm stove, he comes to the top of the hatch and gazes reflectively at the opening. Then an apologetic whine, of which I take no notice. Then a single peremptory bark, very shrill and penetrating, to remind me that he doesn't wish to be kept waiting. I still affect not to hear. Next he shouts blue murder, as though to say, 'Come here at once and lift me down, —— you!' and in sheer self-defence I am forced again to leave my writing-table to oblige him.

He is very fond of me, is Dick, and I am very fond of him, yet I am forced to admit that he is not half so talented as his uncle Michael. Dick is endowed with a considerable amount of what one might call low cunning, but is certainly not clever. His only accomplishment consists in sitting up like an elderly penguin, with his crooked little fore-legs dangling absurdly in the air like a pair of flippers. His hobby ashore is 'dust-binning,' and, on board, investigating the wardroom pantry. In a house, as in the ship, he is always on the wrong side of a door, clamouring impatiently to be let in if he is out, and out if he happens to be in. But he is a very engaging person nevertheless, and has a knowing and rakish appearance. He is white except for his port ear, which is light brown, and has a similarly coloured patch round his starboard eye, which itself is rimmed with black, and consequently looks larger than the port eye, which is edged with pink. The effect is whimsical and striking.

Dick is a well-travelled dog and a very good sailor. In the days when he lived aboard, he went all over the North Sea without turning a hair. Even in a gale of wind in the Skagerrak, where it can blow hard, he was always ready for his victuals.

Michael, the Irish terrier, who lives ashore, hasn't half the breeding of his little nephew, but more than six times his brains. He is getting an old dog now, for it was in October 1909, as a tiny puppy six weeks old, that we first saw him in the cage in the window of a bird-shop not far from Charing Cross Station, to which we had gone to buy a black cat for the ship. (We certainly procure our animals from strange sources, for on another occasion we went to a dogs' home, and emerged with a black cat in a fish-basket.)

Anyhow, we promptly bought Michael for half-a-sovereign, and the same evening I took him off to Sheerness in the pocket of my overcoat to join a destroyer. We have never regretted buying him, for he has lived with us ever since, and has shared the vicissitudes of our married life in the navy, and in the course of his career has visited every naval port in the United Kingdom and a good many other places besides.

He was clever from the very start, and

having been treated more as a human being than as a dog, has developed an intelligence which is almost uncanny. He understands every word that is said to him, and within a few months of our owning him could die for his country and sit up on his haunches and salute his King. He is quite an adept at growling at the mention of certain unpopular personages, concentrating nowadays principally on the Kaiser; while we have only to say, 'Michael, there's a pretty girl passing!' to have him dart to the window, jump on to a chair, and wave his paw. In one set of rooms we inhabited I tired of getting up from the table during meals to ring the bell. It was an old-fashioned bell, not an electric one, so I tied a string to the knob, and a small piece of wood to the end of the string. Then, after twenty minutes' instruction, we had only to say, 'Michael, go and ring the bell!' and the job was done for ever afterwards.

Michael's only real failings are rolling on dead sea-gulls once or twice in the course of a year, but generally just before setting out on a railway journey; digging holes in other people's gardens; and lying on the clean bed-spread in the spare room when we leave the house without him.

But Michael is getting old, and an opaque bluish mist across one of his eyes reminds me constantly that one day he will leave us for ever. I dread the thought of it, for we can never find another like him. He has been our companion in fortune and adversity, always faithful and responsive. People like being loved and admired, and he loves us with a whole-hearted fervour which we perhaps do not deserve. I shall miss his boisterous welcome when I come home from sea. I shall miss the gentle touch of his chin on my knee, and the wistful look in his intelligent brown eyes. Life will never be quite the same without him, for, though I may be a fool so far as dogs are concerned, there never was a dog like Michael.

Hooly, or Hooligan, to give him his full name, belongs to the first lieutenant, and once lived on board as an honorary member of our mess. He is a Dandie Dinmont—his forepart Dandie, and his afterpart Dinmont, as some one once observed—and is dark gray in colour, and is so absurdly long in the body and short in the legs that the men called him 'Old Snakey.' But he was rather a cantankerous person, with a care-worn expression and a knobby liver, so that he also went by the name of 'The fathom of misery.'

When he lived on board he spent most of his leisure barking at sea-gulls, but once developed a mania for following anybody wearing white trousers, with the consequence that when he went ashore in the afternoon during the tennis season he generally lost his master. But he had the wisdom always to stroll down to the landing-place at the time the leave expired, where, unless he was seen by somebody going to his own ship, he embarked in any boat he fancied. In time he visited nearly every destroyer in the flotilla, and frequently went to sea in the wrong ship.

But Hooly is evidently possessed of a *Wanderlust*. He now lives ashore with No. 1's people in Scotland, and one day disappeared completely. He was searched for high and low, but without success. Then came a telegram announcing his whereabouts. The truant had arrived in London by the evening train. Gay dog!

CHAPTER VIII.

THE FINDING OF BOOSTER.

IT had been one of those dull, leaden-coloured days, with an overcast sky and a heavy, tumbling sea—regular North Sea weather. It was our third day out, and for the past twelve hours the wind had been chopping and changing over every point of the compass between north and west. But during the latter part of the afternoon, when a watery, yellow sun shone intermittently between the broken cloud-masses piled up in the western sky, the clerk of the weather seemed to make up his mind once and for all, for the wind veered suddenly to north-north-west, remained steady, and rapidly increased in violence.

It had been blowing hard for some time, and we knew from the ugly look of the sky and the reading of our aneroid—which had been well down towards 28 for thirty-six hours—that we were in for a regular snorter. Our dismal forebodings were speedily justified, for within an hour it was blowing a full gale with all the might and fury of the broad ocean behind it.

We were well out in the middle of the North Sea. What we were doing in that inhospitable region, and in such weather, must perforce remain a secret.

Owing, no doubt, to the previous changeability of the wind, the sea was soon very confused, and the great foaming white-caps came rolling down upon us from no particular direction and in no ordered sequence, but from all points between north and west.   And such seas they were !—huge gray monsters, each with its summit of frothy white, which literally blotted out the horizon when our bows sank into the hollows between them.   There is no more magnificent spectacle than a heavy, breaking sea; no more exhilarating feeling than to know that one's ship and those who man her are pitting their puny strength and skill against the fierce, elemental fury of Nature.   But the best place from which to enjoy the sight is the deck of a large ship, not the spray-swept, reeling bridge of a destroyer battling against the gale.

From fifteen knots we were soon compelled to ease to twelve to avoid damage.   From twelve we reduced to ten, and from ten to eight; but even at this leisurely crawl we bumped badly, as the bows, flung bodily out of the water on the back of some mighty comber, fell into the next abyss with a crash and a thud which shook the whole ship.   And every time they came down tons of water surged across the forecastle in masses ten to fifteen feet deep, to go pouring overboard again in miniature Niagaras as the ship shook herself free.

And the motion—how can I describe it? The nearest approach I can imagine would be

Regular North Sea weather.

PAGE 150.

a switchback railway with the track at varying inclinations up to 40 degrees either side of the horizontal, its alternate hills and valleys thirty feet apart, each dip filled with six feet of water, and a shower-bath all the time. The movement was dizzy and violent, a combined pitching and rolling, lurching and sliding, thudding and crashing, as the ship plunged and wallowed and the seas broke on board. It was a terrible corkscrew motion, which nearly hurled us off our feet, and certainly caused all except our most seasoned shell-backs to retire to the mess-decks, and there to lie, comatose, white-lipped, and utterly dejected, in the throes of the acutest internal discomfort.

Great lumps of solid water, overtopping the rail amidships, came toppling down on deck, to go sweeping aft like liquid avalanches. Occasionally, on glancing aft from the bridge, one could see nothing of the stern save a seething maelstrom of white, with canopies, torpedo-tubes, and other deck fittings appearing here and there like boulders in the bed of a torrent. Life-lines were rigged fore and aft ; but even so, passing along the slippery, reeling deck was an undertaking fraught with no little danger.

We were battened down, but still it was a case of 'water, water everywhere,' even in the wardroom, cabins, mess-deck, and engine-room. As for the charthouse—my inevitable domicile when the ship is at sea, unless I am actually on the bridge—it was long past redemption. Both side - doors were shut, and therefore nominally water-tight, but the water squirted in through many a crevice. It dripped in a steady stream through a faulty pipe-connection in the ceiling, straight on to the settee. A turgid flood went slopping dismally from side to side across the floor with the heavy rolling of the ship, and mingled with it went sundry sodden woollen garments of mine, the remains of a broken tea-cup, the relics of my afternoon meal, a couple of charts in a state of pulpy disintegration, some bound volumes of Sailing Directions and Tide Tables in like condition, most of our navigational instruments, and a bottle of indelible copying-ink with the cork out. It was a joyful sight, but any destroyer officer can supply what details I have missed.

The wind brought the spray flying high over the bridge. It was not ordinary spray in drops, but water in solid, blinding sheets, which left us breathless and gasping. Within five minutes, in spite of oilskins, we felt the moisture trickling slowly down our backs. In half-an-hour our sea-boots were filled and squelching, while in forty minutes we were in such a state of saturation that we could become no wetter unless we actually fell overboard.

Hot food was not to be had, as by some stroke of evil fortune the galley fire had long since been extinguished by a particularly heavy sea, which, breaking on board abreast the foremost funnel, almost filched the whaler from her davits and flooded the galley. But not only was our kitchen *hors de combat ;* so also was the cook.   He, poor wight! had lately joined on from some snug billet in a depot ashore.   He was unused to destroyers and their gyrations, and was lying somewhere amongst that sodden, seasick collection of humanity under the forecastle, and nobody troubled to sort him out and send him about his business. We all knew from bitter experience that ' cookie ' went under in even a capful of wind. He was a broken reed, a fraud, a delusion, and a snare, certainly no seaman, and, like many of his shipmates, would never revive until we drew in under the lee of the land on our homeward journey.

I have no wish to be unkind, for a destroyer's cook, who has to exercise the culinary art for nearly a hundred men in a small galley about eight feet by ten, undoubtedly labours under difficulties undreamt of by any shore-going cook.   But the ancient mariner who called some one else a ' lop-eared son of a sea-cook,' with, of course, the usual nautical embellishments, certainly had some reason for his term of opprobrium.

Our diet had been the same as usual in bad weather—thick sandwiches made with corned beef, ship's biscuits, and cocoa out of vacuum bottles; and glad enough we were to get it.

' Huh!' grunted the first lieutenant, arriving on the bridge at six o'clock to take over the last dog-watch from the sub.   ' This is a mug's game!   Why on earth didn't my people put me into the army?'

' Fool of the family?' I suggested mildly.

'No, sir,' he grinned, retaliating with the time-honoured chestnut as he wrung out his dripping muffler. 'Things have altered since your day.'

'I don't doubt it,' said I. 'I don't profess to be a scientist, like you new-fangled Jacks-of-all-trades from Osborne and Dartmouth. But tell me, what's it like aft?'

'Like, sir!' he snorted. 'There's a foot o' water in the wardroom, and the doctor, in the intervals of trying to rescue his sterilising-gadget, is busy playing leap-frog with the chairs. Every bloomin' one of our gramophone records is smashed, and the deck of the pantry is covered with food and broken crockery, with the stewards lying speechless on top of it! It's a pretty sight, takin' it all round!'

'And what about our flat?' I asked with some anxiety, since No. 1's cabin is opposite to mine and in the same compartment.

'Last time I saw it, it was flooded out,' he answered. 'Your steward was crawling about the deck of your cabin on all fours, rescuing your boots. All your drawers had opened, and most of your shirts, and socks, and books, and things were sculling around on the deck. I told him he'd better get a move on and get the water mopped up, or else you'd probably have his blood; but the poor devil's almost too seasick to move. I rescued your type-writer myself.'

'Are you certain it was the typewriter?' I anxiously asked.

'Quite, sir,' he said cheerfully. 'It had fallen out of its case, and was cruising round about in a pool of water.'

'Damaged?'

'Seemed a bit bent, but I wiped it on your towel and put it on your bunk.'

I thanked him, and groaned aloud, for my typewriter is worth its weight in gold. Sea-water never agrees with the poor thing, and how many times I have taken portions of it to pieces and put them together again I cannot remember.

When we eventually arrived in harbour after this particular trip, I took it wholly to pieces, with the result that it now prints an occasional 'k' instead of a 'g,' 'h' instead of 'e,' and a few other little things of that kind. But it still writes far better than I do, and people who are good at cryptograms are generally able to read its efforts.

The night came down very dàrk, the sky being overcast, and a feeble moon being partly obscured by wisps of low-lying cloud streaming across its surface. With the coming of darkness the gale seemed to increase its fury, for the howling of the wind through our scanty rigging became shriller, the screeching of the squalls more ominous as they drove down upon us. And mingled with the eerie howling, like a booming bass accompaniment, came the mournful, sobbing thunder of the breaking seas, and the steady drumming of the flying spray as it pattered against the painted canvas bridge-screens. It was a wild and dirty night.

There is something awe-inspiring and majestic about the furious orchestra of a gale far out in deep water—something which can be felt in the blood and bone, rather than expressed in mere words. Man may bridge space, harness rivers, and, within limits, change God's configuration of the land; but he can never compel the great ocean to do his bidding, never control the raging of the storm. The sea is ever such a fickle mistress, smiling and gay in her happiness, but quick to anger, and relentless in her passion. She is a thing of whims and fancies, now joyous, now depressed, and always very difficult to please; a merciless enemy, ever eager to reap the advantage of the slightest lapse or most momentary indiscretion on the part of her servants. She is utterly implacable, and rarely forgives a grievance. Sometimes we hate her, for she punishes cruelly—killing, maiming, and drowning our seamen; battering and wrecking our ships; swallowing millions of our money. But even in her fury she fascinates, so that at the back of our minds we really love and respect her. Moreover, it is to the sea, and to the effect that she has had in moulding our national traits and characteristics, that we owe our greatness as an Empire.

Soon after nine o'clock, when we had again reached the southern limit of our patrol, we suddenly sighted a reddish, flickering glare reflected on the underside of the low clouds far away to the southward. And as we watched it danced in and out, now waxing to a lurid crimson, like a splash of blood against the dark background of sea and sky; now waning to a gentle orange glow, like the sheen of the rising moon.

It was a ship on fire. It could be nothing else, though as yet she was still so far over the edge of the horizon that we could see nothing but her flaming advertisement in the sky. But a vessel ablaze in the middle of the North Sea probably meant that some prowling submarine had been at her dirty work, and that even now the wretched survivors might be adrift in open boats, battling for their lives against the fury of the storm. They were a full two hundred miles from the nearest land. It might have been two million, for all the chance they had of reaching it.

Our leader at once altered course towards the glare, and we followed round in her wake.

'Fifteen knots,' came her signal, winking from ship to ship.

'Twenty knots,' a few minutes later, as we swung into line astern of her.

There was still a chance of saving lives, still a remote possibility that Fritz might yet be lurking near the scene of his evil handiwork.

But I shivered to think of what might already have been the fate of the crew of that ship; for the vessel, judging from the blaze, had been alight for many hours. They must long since have taken to their boats; but how could they live in such a turmoil? Even the sturdy old *Triptolemus*, with the gale astern of her, plunged and wallowed like a mad thing as she took the seas in her stride, and, yawing drunkenly in her course, slid giddily down the liquid valleys with propellers racing and the water bubbling and frothing deep over the forecastle.

There is something very exhilarating in steaming fast in a destroyer with the wind and a heavy sea astern. One feels the ship being hurled bodily forward with a swift rush like an arrow as the afterpart rears up and the bows go under, while the next moment the stern falls into a trough and the speed seems to lessen as the forepart goes tobogganing along on the back of a huge breaking sea. There is no sensation quite equal to it, but it takes a tricky helmsman to keep a vessel anywhere near her course in such conditions.

Our rush through the night towards that burning ship is indelibly stamped upon my memory. It was the first fire at sea I had ever witnessed—but not the last, for before we had gone very far we sighted another blaze on the horizon, perhaps eight miles to the eastward of the first. Two burning ships in one night within half-a-score miles of each other—Fritz had certainly been busy!

A magnificent spectacle the first ship presented as we approached and circled round to investigate. She was a large, barque-rigged vessel, deeply laden with timber, and, with her fore and main topsail set and her helm evidently lashed, still sailed on before the wind, yawing wildly as she went. Her slender hull,

She was ablaze from end to end.

PAGE 158.

silhouetted as black as ebony against the ruddy reflection on the water, rolled and pitched heavily, now and then to disappear entirely in the deep troughs between the waves. Her deck was ablaze from end to end, a raging inferno of flame, so that her masts seemed to be standing erect out of a sea of fire. The flames leapt and played about her, sometimes darting as high as her tops, occasionally streaming to leeward like the tail of a comet. We could see flickering streaks of fire mounting higher and higher in her tarred rigging, and the canvas of her furled sail smouldering redly and bursting into bright flame. Masts, yards, and rigging, indeed, were outlined in vivid scarlet, like some gigantic set-piece at a firework display.

A billowing cloud of smoke, tinged crimson and orange, and mingled with sudden rushes of brilliant sparks and larger fragments of blazing débris, went rolling away to leeward in a dense, impalpable curtain which blotted out the horizon. Above the howling of the gale we could hear the roaring crash and crackle of the fire, and the hiss and splutter of the seas as they sprayed on board and vanished in steam. Sea and sky alike were dyed a light crimson-orange, and even three cables or more to windward the heat was intense enough to be uncomfortable.

Then the mainmast burned through, swayed drunkenly for a moment as the ship rolled, and tumbled with a crash and a swift shower of sparks. It was followed in turn by the fore and

the mizzen masts, until presently that once tall
and stately barque was nothing but a blazing
hull on the wild waste of waters, a mute,
flaming testimony to the senseless passion of
war. Fire and water fought avidly for her
mastery, but fire would hold its own until she
burned to the water's edge and became a charred
derelict.

Her boats had gone ; but though we searched
the vicinity, swept the sea with searchlights,
and cruised to and fro with our eyes and
glasses busy, we could find no trace of any
survivors. It was not until we had given up
the search as hopeless, and were steaming
towards the second vessel, indeed, that suddenly, far to the southward, we saw a flickering, dancing, glimmer of light.

'Take its bearing, some one!' I shouted
instinctively.

'South ten east,' said the first lieutenant,
bending down to run his eye along the compass, as the light waned to a faint sparkle,
and then vanished altogether.

'That'll be a boat,' I said. 'They've
spotted our searchlights.'

An instant later came a signal from our
leader: 'Close light to the southward and
investigate,' she said ; and hard a-starboard,
and away we went.

Finding that light was like hunting a will-
o'-the-wisp, for, though we knew its original
bearing, it flickered into being only at long
and irregular intervals, shone dimly for a
moment, and then was suddenly eclipsed.

It was, as we discovered afterwards, a home-made flare of teased-out rope-yarn, soaked in oil, and lashed to a boat-hook stave. In the boat was a single sodden box of matches with which to ignite it; so, what with the difficulty of striking a light when the boat fell into comparative calm in the troughs of the waves, shielding the feeble flicker from the drenching spray and the raging wind as she rose on the crests, and then applying it to the damp torch and nursing the latter into flame, it seems very wonderful that they got it to burn at all. Their supply of matches was perilously low, and time and time again the flare was raised aloft, only to be extinguished immediately by wind and spray.

But the survivors had seen our light, and knew that help was at hand if only they could attract our attention. They persisted in their efforts; and well it was that they did so, for it was only due to these sudden sparks in the wild blackness of the night that we were able to find them.

'Saved by a box of matches!' Quite a stirring title for a melodrama at the 'movies;' but it was only a box of matches that prevented this particular affair from becoming another tragedy of the sea.

And so, fifteen miles to leeward, we eventually came across a boat crowded with men. Even now our difficulties had not altogether vanished. There was only one possible method of rescuing them, and that was by placing the *Triptolemus* herself between the boat and the wind, and keeping her there. From this position the ship could give the boat something of a lee, and could drift down upon her until she was close alongside, when the occupants would have to scramble aboard with the ropes' ends that we should have ready for them. It was taking a risk—rather a big risk, for the ship, with the sea broad on the bow, would roll and plunge madly, so that there was always the danger of the boat being capsized and every soul in her flung into the water. But it was neck or nothing. It simply had to be done.

The helm went over, and the port engine went astern, to bring the ship round short on her heel. She answered nobly, for there was a brief respite, followed by the thundering crash of three heavy seas breaking on board in quick succession as she came broadside on to the sea. And how she rolled! Fifty degrees either way, without exaggeration, until we could scarcely stand on the bridge, while the lee edge of the upper deck went under, and we could see the white water creaming and surging round the bases of the funnels.

Presently the boat was close alongside, poised dizzily on the swirling crest of a wave at one moment, and the next sinking deep into a hollow, until she was hidden out of sight of the bridge somewhere under the curve of the hull. Many times we held our breath in suspense, expecting to see her stove in and swamped as the ship lurched drunkenly towards her, or else carried bodily inboard and capsized as she rose on a sea and the lee edge of the deck dipped under water.

But the men did their work well. They fended her off without mishap, and one by one, watching their opportunity, the occupants leapt to safety, or were dragged on board with ropes' ends. There were sixteen of them all told—sixteen and Booster—the entire crew of one of the burning ships, and happy enough they were to be rescued. They were scantily clad, wet through to the skin, perishing with cold, and very much exhausted; but our men, tender-hearted as usual, vied with each other in forcing their spare garments upon them. Indeed, it was not very long before our guests, full of hot grog, ship's biscuit, and the inevitable salmon and corned beef, were smoking cigarettes on the mess-deck, snug and warm in their borrowed finery. Their distressing ordeal had certainly not affected their appetites.

We should have liked to salve the boat, for she was a stoutly built craft fitted with a motor; but the stories we had heard of German submarines lurking in the vicinity of boats with survivors aboard, with the idea of torpedoing any vessel which came to their assistance, effectually prevented our remaining in one place for any longer than was absolutely necessary. So we left her drifting, and steamed back to rejoin our mates.

Until dawn we scanned the sea for the survivors of the other vessel, zigzagging to and fro and covering many miles; but our efforts were unsuccessful. They seemed to

have vanished completely from off the face
of the waters, and to this day we have never
heard what became of them.

It was the same old story that our survivors
afterwards told us; a tale of utter callousness
and indifference to suffering—of what, indeed,
practically amounted to wilful murder on the
high seas.

'We were sailing along quite peacefully,'
said the master, spinning us his yarn in the
wardroom, 'when, just about noon on the day
you picked us up, an ugly gray brute of a
submarine suddenly appeared on the surface
about a couple o' miles away to starboard.
We'd nothing to fight with, no guns or any-

thing, and couldn't escape; so we just backed
our maintops'l to heave the ship to, and
waited.   But within a minute, though she
must have seen what we were about, she was
blazing away with her guns, and the shell
came whistling overhead and flopping into
the water all round.'

Some one interrupted him to ask a few
leading questions about the size of the gun
and the accuracy of the shooting.

'Never hit us once, except with splinters,'
he answered.   'That wasn't their fault, though.
They fired to hit—we could see that all right.
So I ordered the boat out, put food and water
into her, got the men aboard, got into her
myself, and pulled away from the ship.   Then
they started lobbing shell at us in the boat,
and Heaven alone knows why they didn't hit
us.   Anyhow, they stopped firing after a bit,
and came close alongside, pointing rifles and
revolvers at our heads, and jeering like fools.
"You can put the damned things down,"
says I.   "You needn't be afraid; we're quite

unarmed."—"The captain and the mate are to come aboard," says an officer on the submarine's conning-tower, speaking excellent English.

'So we went aboard, the mate and I, and they demanded to see our papers, and asked all sorts of questions; but I don't think they got much worth knowing. "What food have you got in the boat?" the officer asks.— "Food!" says I. "You didn't give us much of a chance to get food!"—"That is just as well," he says, with an ugly laugh. "We want food ourselves, and might have borrowed yours! I 've a mind to make you prisoners," that German officer goes on to say to the mate and me, scratching his chin. "If I hadn't so many other Englishmen aboard, I would take you back to Germany."

'I said nothing to that, because I couldn't think of anything to say. "Why the hell don't you answer me, you pig dog?" he suddenly shouts, mouthing like a madman, and fumbling with his pistol.—"What can I answer?" I asks him, beginning to see red, and longing to hit him in the face. He scowled at me and rapped out an order, and before I properly knew what was up, one of his men got into our boat, got hold of our water-barricoe, and emptied it overboard. "There," the officer snarls; "that'll teach you a lesson, you English swine!"—"You 're murdering us!" says I, longing to get at him, though I knew there was another small water-tank built into the boat, which he hadn't spotted. "And what the hell do I care?" he sneers. "This is war, and my men will destroy your ship."—"Go on," I told him, a bit sarcastic; "there's plenty more where she came from." That was stupid of me, because he glared at me like a maniac, and pointed his pistol at my middle. I quite thought my number was up.

'However, he didn't shoot, and presently the boat goes back to the ship, leaving the mate and me aboard the submarine. Four Germans with pistols and bombs went in the boat, and after collaring all the grub they could find, they upset paraffin and petrol over the deck, and set a match to it. Presently there was an explosion or two, and I could see the ship was starting to burn. The boat then came back, and the Germans got out of her, and made our men hand out the tinned grub the blighters had stolen. "Get back into your boat," says the lieutenant to the mate and me, "and think yourselves lucky we have spared your lives!"—"Spared our lives!" says I. "There's bad weather coming on, and we shall never reach the land."—"Get into your boat!" he shouts, waving his pistol again. "What do I care if you don't reach the land? Get your own damned navy to help you! This is war! My ship is not a hotel for swine like you!" That officer was a fair corker, and could swear in English like a Thames bargee!

'Well, we got into the boat, and he got on to his conning-tower, and the submarine made

off on the surface, with all her men laughing
and jeering at us. "I will report the destruction of your ship!" was the last thing the
officer called out to me. "Perhaps you will
not have an opportunity to do it yourself. If
you do get back, present my regards to the
English Navy and to Sir Lloyd George, and
tell 'em they 'll all be starving in six months'
time." He was a perfect gent, that he was!
Then the submarine steamed off to the north-
eastward, towards another ship which was in
sight, and an hour or two later we saw they 'd
set her on fire as well.

'You know the rest, gentlemen,' he went
on. 'It was blowing fairly hard when we
took to the boat, but towards the end of the
afternoon it started to blow great guns. We
rigged a sea-anchor, and put canvas round the
gunwale to increase the freeboard; but she
was so deep in the water with the men she
had aboard that we shipped a terrible lot of
water, and had to bale for all we were worth.

'Then it got dark, and there was nothing
in sight except those two burning ships. It
was a pretty dismal prospect for us, I can tell
you, for all the time the wind was increasing
and the sea getting worse. Water kept coming
on board, and before long the boat was full
up to the thwarts. Presently the rope to
the sea-anchor chafed through and the anchor
carried away. We started in to say our
prayers then, for we thought we were goners.
But then, thank God! we suddenly saw your
searchlights, and set to work to make our

flare. We never thought you'd see it, for we'd drifted so far to leeward; but a bit later we spotted your red and green lights bearing down towards us, and when'—— He hesitated.

'I don't know if you've ever given up all hope, and then suddenly realised that your life is going to be saved, gentlemen,' he concluded huskily, 'but we could have shouted for joy when we saw you coming. We—well, we are very grateful to you, gentlemen—far more grateful than I can possibly tell you. We couldn't have lasted for more than another hour with that sea running. You saved our lives.'

'Pure good luck that we happened to be on the spot,' we assured him, quite truthfully, for it was more by good fortune than anything else, and no merit was attributable to us.

'Ay, that may be,' he agreed, with a nod. 'But if you hadn't turned up, we should have gone the way of a good many others; and, believe me, gentlemen, we are very grateful.'

His tale was told in a simple, seaman-like manner, with a complete absence of flowery language and ornamental flourish. But he was obviously sincere, and the look of gratitude in his eyes was more than ample reward for the little service that we had rendered.

In due course we landed the survivors, but Booster remained with us as a substantial memento of the occasion.

Now, Booster is a dog, an enormous creature, rather like one of Jack London's 'huskies,' with the build of a wolf. He weighs, to hazard a wild guess, something between ninety and a hundred pounds, and has a heavy, lupine head, a pair of the gentlest brown eyes I have ever seen, a curling, bushy tail, and a very thick coat, dark gray on the outside and cream-colour beneath. Altogether a very engaging person, he rapidly became acclimatised to his new surroundings, though in the early days of his naval career he developed a passion for desertion. On one occasion, indeed, he absented himself from his place of duty for fully a week, during which we spent no small portion of our time and money in inditing reply-paid telegrams to the police authorities, and in concocting advertisements for insertion in the local newspapers.

In reply to various inquiries, we received the following communication from the chief constable :

'*Re* Dog Booster,' it started. 'I beg to state that, in accordance with your telegrams and letters, the Dog Booster was discovered wandering at large in the town at 7.30 A.M. on the 17th instant. He was conducted to the Police Station, and was secured with a piece of rope. After partaking of a hearty breakfast, he slipped his collar and escaped. I much regret this most unfortunate circumstance, but the Police are on his track, and I will communicate with you further when the dog is found.—Yours faithfully, ——.

'*P.S.*—The collar may be obtained on application at the Police Station.'

Happy thought, that postscript ! But what,

I ask you, is the good of a collar without a dog to put inside it?

However, with the assistance of a friend, who knew the assistant provost-marshal, the truant was eventually run to earth and apprehended by the military police, whereupon we received a telegram.

'Dog Booster now in custody at ——,' it ran. 'Please send escort when convenient.'

So the escort was sent, and the deserter brought back at the end of a chain. We were pleased to see him; but he hadn't even the grace to look ashamed of himself, though his escapade had cost me a pretty penny for telegrams, rewards, and advertisements.

Up to this time I was not aware that the apprehension of dog deserters was included in the duties of the military police, but the corps seem capable of turning their hands to anything, and certainly did us a good turn on this occasion.

But I am glad I am not an A.P.M., for his work is certainly no sinecure. He requires the temper of a parliamentary candidate and the wisdom of a Solomon.

Once, at a place not so very far from where these words will be printed, a bluejacket, a private in a kilted regiment, and an Australian soldier forgathered and made merry together, and in the course of their afternoon's amusement repaired to a photographer's and had their portraits taken. Having done so, they conceived the brilliant notion of repeating the process in each other's clothes; so the blue-jacket arrayed himself in the kilt, the Scotsman in the uniform of the Australian, and the last-named assumed the jumper and bell-bottomed trousers of the sailor. But they had looked upon the beer when it was so very golden that they quite forgot to change back again, while on leaving the photographer's they made merrier still.

And towards evening the sleuth-hounds of the military police came upon three very hilarious members of His Majesty's forces, staggering arm-in-arm down the roadway; whereupon they—the hilarious ones—were arrested and incarcerated for the night. The next morning, when the culprits were still too hazy and heavy-headed to give any satisfactory account of themselves, their garments were searched for documents of evidence, and they were despatched under escort to their several destinations. Unfortunately they were the wrong destinations; for the naval authorities presently found themselves in possession of a vituperant gentleman from the Antipodes, the C.O. of the Scottish battalion at Dumfries with a horny-handed son of the sea in a kilt and a sporran, and the Australian C.O., on Salisbury Plain, I think it was, with an excited and rather unintelligible Scot.

I leave it at that. Who would not be a military policeman?

CHAPTER IX.

THE STORY OF MATTHEW CONOLLY.*

I.

A CASUAL inspection of the smiling, rubicund countenance of Matthew Conolly, sometime skipper, Royal Naval Reserve, would hardly have led one to believe that there had been any sadness in his life.

Imagine a man in the late thirties—a short, stocky, deep-chested little man with rather bowed legs, a typically rolling walk, a voice like a bull, and a deep-throated laugh like the baying of a bloodhound. His clean-shaven face was tanned the colour of deep mahogany by wind and spray. He possessed a thick thatch of curly hair, graying a little over the temples, an everlasting golden stubble on his cheeks and chin which no razor ever seemed wholly to remove, a pair of twinkling gray eyes half-hidden behind bushy, untidy eyebrows, and a perpetual smile.

It was his smile, indeed, which was most attractive, for somehow his mirth was so genuine and spontaneous that it became infectious. At one moment he would be looking at you with a rapt expression—his head sideways, with one ear cocked forward

---

* The incidents here described, though fictitious, are truly typical of the part being constantly played by our brave fishermen-volunteers.

like a listening dog. Then would come a
slow wrinkling of his chubby face and a
screwing up of his eyes. Next came a short,
explosive bark, followed by the deep, gurgling
'Huh! huh! huh!' of his laughter.

He laughed whole-heartedly with his mouth
open, so that you could see his white, even
teeth. He laughed because he was really
amused, not out of mere politeness at somebody else's joke; and however down in the
dumps you might be feeling, you were, somehow, constrained to laugh with him.

The first time I met him was in a railway
carriage, where, as Dick, the Sealyham, was
occupying his usual travelling billet, a portion
of the luggage-rack overhead, we came into
conversation about dogs. Thence we drifted
on to the sea, to ships, and to Matthew Conolly
himself, he volunteering the information that
he was off on seven days' leave to visit his
wife and child, who lived somewhere up the
line.

I did not take kindly to his clothes, I must
admit. He was resplendent in mufti—a wonderful brown suit, blue-spotted necktie, a stiff
white collar constricting his bull-neck, and a
pair of the shiniest brown boots I had ever
seen. He clutched a pair of brown-kid gloves
and a silver-mounted walking-stick in one
calloused, sunburnt hand, and held a cigar in
the other. A black billycock hat, rather too
small for him, was perched on his head, while
the 'southern' portion of his white waistcoat
was adorned with what a jeweller would call

Matthew Conolly.

PAGE 174.

a 'massive gold albert' almost the size of a ship's cable. It was summer, and at intervals he mopped his shiny face with a purple-silk handkerchief.

It did not need the acumen of a Sherlock Holmes to name him a seaman the moment one saw him. There was no mistaking the tanned, leathery appearance of his skin, and the network of tiny puckers and wrinkles round the corners of his eyes. And even if one missed the significance of these, there was always the faint blue anchor tattooed on his right wrist. Moreover, his high collar and shiny boots caused him obvious discomfort, which showed clearly enough that he was used to homelier attire.

And so, being carriage-mates for an hour, we talked of dogs, ships, the sea, the war—all manner of things, including the growing of sweet-peas and potatoes. He told me proudly of his wife and 'little nipper.' He spun the yarns of some of his adventures at sea during the war—adventures which knocked my hum-drum experiences into a cocked hat. And at times there came that deep, infectious laugh of his, which made me laugh with him.

The next time I saw him his shiny red face was framed in the wheelhouse window of a steam-trawler elbowing her way into a lock crowded with many others of her species. She was a disreputable-looking little trawler called the *Guiding Hope*. Her hull was streaked with rust, her funnel caked with spray-salt, and her ensign blackened and unrecognisable.

Only the little gun mounted on its platform abaft the funnel was really clean. And her men were thoroughly in keeping with their vessel. They looked a veritable gang of pirates, and all of them, except the wireless operator, a beardless youth of the R.N.V.R., to whom a razor was not a necessity, gave abundant evidence that they had omitted to shave for several days. But what else could one expect when their little ship had just come in from the patrol-grounds of the North Sea?

'Good-afternoon, Mr Conolly,' I hailed him when his vessel was safely secured.

'Good-afternoon,' he answered, screwing up his face to remember who on earth I was, and where we had met.

'Did you have a good leave?' I asked.

'Ah!' he said with a smile; 'now I remembers. You're the gent wi' the li'l' dawg in the railway carriage. How's the li'l' dawg?'

'Very well, thanks.'

'What you done wi' him?' he wanted to know. 'Nice li'l' dawg, he was.'

'He's at home,' I answered. 'I hope you found your wife and child quite well, and that you had a good time yourself.'

'Middlin' good, thank 'ee,' he grunted, scrambling ashore. 'But seven days' leave isn't much good to a man like me. All the time I keeps sayin' to meself, "Only six days more," "Only three days more." I counts every minute; and what wi' hoein' the garden, plantin' the vegetables, an' playin' wi' the kid, my leave is up before I properly realise it's started.'

I nodded in sympathy, for I was afflicted in the same way myself. Leave, in these days of war and strenuousness, is all too short.

And for a time, until the lock-gates opened, and with a screeching and a hooting on their whistles the group of trawlers scrambled through like a flock of sheep into the basin beyond, we walked up and down the jetty, yarning away about the things which interested us. He told a good story, did Matthew Conolly, and had a droll way of telling it.

I met him many times after that, and learned something of his history. He was one of those men who improve vastly on acquaintance, and I must say I liked him much better dressed in his simple naval uniform than in the rather flamboyant garments he affected as a civilian and a gentleman at large.

He was an orphan, and had never known his parents. His childhood had been spent with the family of his maternal uncle, and for the first five years of his life all went well, for his uncle and aunt brought him up as their own son, and came to love him. Then his aunt died, and the widower married a masterful lady of dubious charm and uncertain temper, who cordially detested Matthew. Later on, when more children arrived, he was the black sheep in the fold and an interloper, and more than once his sturdy independence of spirit involved him in serious trouble with his 'aunt-in-law.' She behaved harshly to him, and never gave him a fair chance, while there was always a subtle difference between his treatment and that of his cousins. It was not a question of money, for Matthew's uncle Timothy, a grocer with a good connection, was tolerably well endowed with this world's goods; but although the cousins were well dressed and cared for, Matthew's clothes were always thin and threadbare, and his boots full of holes. The other children were sent to private and most genteel 'scholastic establishments,' where they were taught dancing and deportment, but he picked up what little knowledge he could at the Board School.

His uncle, completely under his wife's thumb, was either too timid or too busy to remonstrate.

One would not dwell upon these details were it not for the fact that these early years of hardship and cruelty must have had a great effect in forming Matthew's character. They taught him independence and how to fend for himself; and at the age of thirteen, after a particularly stormy interview with his aunt, he marched out of the house without a penny in his pocket, and deliberately cut himself off from the only relations he had in the world, never to return.

Uncle Timothy, to do him justice, tried to induce the truant to come back, and, when this failed, offered to finance him. But Matthew's reply was characteristic.

'DERE UNCLE,' he wrote in his scarcely

legible hand, 'I have gone on a ship and am happy here. I don't want no money. Tell aunt I won't come back.   MATTHEW.'

And three years later the uncle died, and the boy was left without a real friend in the world.

II.

In spite of his step-aunt's prognostications, Matthew flourished exceedingly. He started his career as a fisherman with everything against him, and without influence of any sort or a soul in the world to give him a helping hand. He was the lowliest of the lowly. By the time he was twenty-one, however, partly perhaps by luck, but due more largely to his own dogged determination, indomitable pluck, and inherent capacity for hard work, he had become the 'second hand' of a steam-trawler, his skipper's trusted second in command and right-hand man.

He seemed, somehow, to possess a natural, inborn instinct for the sea, that lucky quality which enables men to know the North Sea even as the palms of their own hands, to gauge with certainty the whereabouts and the habits of the fish, and to grope their way in and out of the fog-wreathed fastnesses of the fishing-grounds with no sight of the sun, and nothing but an occasional cast of the lead to guide them. It is an instinct, nothing more or less; but with some men, especially North Sea fishermen, it is as unerring as the sense which enables a dog to single out his master in a crowd, or to know his way home from a distance. Matthew, moreover, had already passed what examinations were necessary to qualify him for a command of his own. He was hard-headed and thrifty, too, so that he saved money and forged ahead while others still lingered by the wayside.

People thought well of him professionally, and realised that he was a man with a future ; but he was not spoilt by his popularity.

Soon after his twenty-fourth birthday his opportunity came, for old Amos Buckley, the skipper of the *Guiding Hope*, was swept overboard and drowned in heavy weather on the Dogger, and Matthew stepped permanently into the dead man's shoes.

Within three years he was part owner of the *Guiding Hope*, and had acquired a substantial interest in various other craft. He had bought and furnished a house, and then, in his usual methodical way, had cast around for a wife. He soon found one, a gentle-voiced, soft little woman who loved him with every fibre of her being. And secure in the affection of a woman whom he idolised, and who possessed the unfailing knack of drawing out everything that was good in him, Matthew, who had never known a mother's love, discovered a new happiness and savour in life. Gone were the bitterness and drudgery of existence. He now had something tangible to live and to strive for, something that increased a thousandfold when John Conolly, his son, made his appearance.

When the war came and the call went

forth for volunteers to man the fishing-craft taken over by the Admiralty for use as mine-sweepers and patrol-vessels, Matthew, with many others, proffered his services. The powers that be accepted him gladly, presenting him with a warrant as skipper, R.N.R., and the wherewithal to purchase a blue uniform suit with brass buttons, and a peaked cap with a gold badge embellished with laurel-leaves, a royal crown, and the foul anchor. They appointed him, moreover, in command of his own *Guiding Hope*, informed him gaily that he was liable to trial by court-martial if he ran her ashore or collided with another vessel, and gave him to understand that he was now an officer of His Majesty's Navy, with all the might and power of the Service to back him up, and to help him to enforce a new and wholly unfamiliar discipline upon those he commanded. But his crew, when they heard of these things, merely laughed. They became positively apoplectic with amusement the first time he appeared among them in the glory of his naval uniform, and opinions were divided as to whether he should be addressed as 'your worship,' 'Mr Conolly,' with the accent on the 'Mister,' or merely 'sir.'

And Matthew, for his part, became answerable for all his doings to those set in authority over him, beings resplendent in gold lace, who sat in offices ashore and dictated orders in a terse, decisive way which rather jarred on his nerves until he got used to it. They were

regular naval officers, whom he had to call
'sir;' officers in whose presence he was expected to doff his headgear, and whose orders
had to be carried out to the very letter without question or demur. They treated him
with respect, however, addressing him always
as 'Mister Conolly,' a civility to which he was
quite unaccustomed.

He soon became acclimatised to his new
mode of life, and speedily discovered that his
seniors, for all their brusquerie and occasional
asperity, had an intense sympathy with, and
understanding of, those who, like himself, had
offered their little all in the service of their
country. They were out to help and to
advise, to get the utmost out of their subordinates without offending their susceptibili-
ties; but woe betide the laggards, or those
who did not do their job!

And lo! in course of time, when Matthew
found himself bereft of his own personality
and absorbed into a multitude of skippers
from Hull, the Tyne, Aberdeen, and Fleet-
wood—men speaking every dialect of the
British Isles, but all employed in the great
game of strafing the Hun—he found the
work greatly to his liking. It was scarcely
more strenuous than life in peace-time, for
they worked to a hard-and-fast routine of
so many days at sea, followed by a shorter
period in harbour. They no longer fished,
but some were employed on sweeping the
fairways clear of mines for the passage of
the mercantile traffic up and down the coast,

while others were despatched farther afield to patrol the spots where Fritz, the German submarine, might strive to carry on his evil handiwork. Sometimes it was dull and monotonous, at others intensely exciting; but it was always risky, and Matthew delighted in it.

The *Guiding Hope* was now a man-of-war, provided with a White Ensign and an evil little six-pounder Hotchkiss gun. Her men, who had signed on *en bloc* for the trawler section of the Royal Naval Reserve, were subject to the Naval Discipline Act, and wore naval uniforms, albeit they still exhibited a partiality for coloured mufflers, ancient tweed trousers, and unspeakable blue jerseys when their senior officers were not about. They drew their naval rations—beef, bread, and vegetables; jam—which did not appeal to their hardened palates; and good, honest naval rum, which warmed the cockles of their hearts. It was the rum, indeed, which involved Matthew in his first little contretemps with the authorities, and, to judge from his own description of the episode, the scene must have been rather diverting.

It appears that they obtained six weeks' allowance of stores at a time, and, in their supreme ignorance of the King's Regulations and Admiralty Instructions, successfully disposed of the rum in ten days. It was good stuff, that rum, and a glass of it, hot and mixed with very little water, was very comforting before turning in, wet through and tired after a night-watch on deck.

'My good sir!' exclaimed a rather excited and very purple-faced victualling paymaster when he came to scrutinise the *Guiding Hope's* accounts, 'you seem to have issued the spirit ration when and how you liked! Don't you realise that the allowance is half a gill per man per day?'

'Can't say I did, sir,' answered Matthew, smiling in his inimitable way. 'I don't know them regulations; and, besides, we never had nothing to measure it with. I serve it out in an or'nary half-pint tumbler—half a glass at midday, and another half when they wants it.'

The paymaster's eyes protruded visibly from his head. 'Lord, Mr Conolly!' he gasped, 'did they remain fairly sober?'

'Sober, sir! Of course they did. A little drop like that wouldn't hurt them. They're not children!'

The naval officer breathed heavily. 'They must be pretty hard cases,' he went on. 'However, I can square it up this time; but for Heaven's sake don't get doing such things again, or you'll get us both into serious trouble. You draw six weeks' allowance at a time, remember—just sufficient to keep you going by issuing the strict service ration. Good-morning.'

So Matthew, rather perplexed, retired.

Really, the Royal Navy was a peculiar sort of profession, and until he got used to it he often found himself butting up against its strange customs and traditions. Who was to know, for instance, that it was not customary for an officer to partake of liquid refreshment in a quayside hostelry with his men; that one must not wear a pin in one's tie or a flower in one's button-hole in uniform; and that it was the correct thing for a junior officer to enter a boat first and to leave it last, ignorance of which piece of naval etiquette involved him in a slight difference of opinion with a retired and rather peppery officer wearing three rows of gold lace?

Then there was the huge tome called *The King's Regulations and Admiralty Instructions*, a massive compilation which even laid down the correct length for the men's whiskers and the dimensions of their trousers, and made Matthew feel quite dizzy to look at. So he merely glanced at it once, locked it carefully in a cupboard for safe keeping, and, like a wise man, never opened the book again.

'I reckon them regulations wasn't put together for the likes o' me,' he observed with a twinkle in his eye.

I am inclined to agree, for, from what I saw and heard of him, I should imagine that Matthew Conolly was a law unto himself.

III.

Several times during the night the low, pulsating throb of distant gun-fire, borne seaward on the gentle offshore breeze, had sounded from the westward. Sometimes the upper sky in the same direction sparkled and scintillated with a myriad tiny dancing flashes, now orange, now ruby-red, as anti-aircraft shell soared upwards and burst. Occasionally the arch of the heavens was illuminated by the bluish-white beams of many searchlights, miles away over the edge of the horizon, which opened and closed, rose and fell, like the exploring fingers of some giant hand.

Once or twice the deep, rumbling thuds of heavier explosions came to the ear like rolls of distant thunder. They were caused by bombs—Zeppelin bombs; but their detonation in no way disturbed the equanimity of those on board the *Guiding Hope*, stationed on her patrol at no great distance from the coast.

It was 1918. The war had been in progress for nearly four years, and men serving in the North Sea had long since become accustomed to air-raids and other abominations of war. For all the notice they took of the illumination in the sky, indeed, it might have been an innocent firework display.

During the afternoon the air had suddenly become turgid with wireless as the vessels on the outlying patrols reported the raiding Zeppelins approaching the coast. Some time after sunset, moreover, those on board the *Guiding Hope* had counted no fewer than five of the huge, sausage-shaped monsters sharply silhouetted against the darkening evening sky. They had come streaming in from the east-ward in a rough V-shaped formation like a gaggle of geese at flighting-time. They were flying at a good twelve thousand feet, but their advent did not pass unreported.

And now, at half-past two in the morning,

the dawn was slowly breaking out over the eastern sky, and Matthew, rather sleepy about the eyes, and swathed to the neck in a variety of woollen garments and mufflers, watched through his wheelhouse window the blackness of night slowly giving way to the brilliance of daylight. He held a large basin of steaming cocoa in one hand, and a lighted pipe in the other, and alleviated the monotony of his watch by alternate gulps of the hot liquid and puffs at his pipe.

'I wonder where them things have got to,' he grunted to the helmsman beside him, screwing his head round to probe the still dark horizon to the west. 'There hasn't been no firin' ashore this couple of hours or more.'

The scant discipline and the rather free-and-easy methods which obtained on board the *Guiding Hope* would scarcely have passed muster on board the smallest regular man-of-war of His Majesty's Navy. But then the *Guiding Hope* was not a regular man-of-war. She was distinctly irregular, and rather prided herself on being a paid volunteer. Moreover, Matthew had known most of his crew for years. He had grown up with them, so to speak, and the fact that the ship now flew the White Ensign instead of the Red was no reason for his changing the habits of a lifetime. His men's affairs were his affairs, and as often as not he addressed them by their Christian names. Except when there was work in hand, he treated them with an easy familiarity which would have caused the most junior midshipman of the Royal Navy to observe that discipline had gone to the dogs. But discipline, in its outward and visible sense, at any rate, had never existed on the *Guiding Hope*, and I do not think she suffered much through the lack of it. The hearts of her men were essentially in the right place, particularly when there was work in hand.

'They 're 'alf-way 'ome by this time !' opined the man at the wheel, an incorrigible pessimist. 'We never seem to 'ave no luck nowadays !'

'What! in bringin' 'em down, George?' Matthew queried.

'Ay. Shootin' 'em down, like the murderin' swine they are ! Bin killin' a lot more inner-cent wimmin an' kids this trip, I s'pose !'

The skipper noisily disposed of the dregs of his cocoa, and wiped his mouth on the back of his hand ; but further conversation was broken short by the opening of the door and the entry of the wireless operator.

'We 've been ordered to look out for damaged Zeppelins, sir !' he exclaimed, thrust-ing forth a paper.

'Ah, that's a bit more like it !' grunted Matthew, his face beaming. 'Read out what they says, boy.'

'"To all ships and auxiliary patrol-vessels,"' the youth read. '"Look out for two Zeppelins damaged by gun-fire. Last reported steering east in area nineteen. Flying low."'

'Zeppelins !' the helmsman suddenly burst out. 'And if that ain't one o' the skulkin'

swabs comin' out o' that dull patch on the
'orizon I 'll give any one a pound o' 'bacca!'
He released the wheel and pointed with an air
of suppressed excitement to the westward.

The skipper looked up, seized his binoculars,
and levelled them in the direction indicated.
'Holy smoke, George!' he muttered, after the
briefest inspection; 'you 're right. That 's
one of 'em, sure 'nough!'

'Course I'm right, skipper,' grinned the irrepressible George, with ill-concealed triumph.
''Aven't you always said I got the best pair o'
eyes in the ship?'

Matthew had made no such wild statement,
but was now far too preoccupied to pay attention to George's vapourings.

'Hard a-starboard!' he ordered hurriedly,
still busy with the glasses. 'Steer straight for
her, George!—You, boy,' turning to the wireless operator—'you go down an' tell Moxon
an' the others to have the gun ready. Tell
'em we may want the boat, too!'

The operator disappeared as the *Guiding
Hope* swung round.

Now, a Zeppelin in flight high in the air
and a Zeppelin seen close to the surface are
two very different objects. The first is reduced
by space to almost miniature dimensions; but
this one, with her great yellow length floating
at an angle of nearly forty-five degrees, and
her stern a bare hundred and fifty feet above
the water, seemed, as they approached her,
literally to block out the horizon. She loomed
monstrous and ungainly through the slight

morning haze, bigger by far than the largest ship ever dreamt of.

She was still struggling to ascend, circling round and round like a winged bird—sometimes broadside on, now heading towards them, now away. She was evidently badly damaged, and the end was not far distant, for even as they watched she was slowly sinking, while her pointed stern dipped lower and lower as the blunt, unwieldy bow reared itself heavenwards.

The *Guiding Hope*, quivering like a jelly as the men in her stokehold plied their shovels and the engineers opened the throttles wide, was coming up hand over fist. But away to the west-north-west a cloud of smoke heralded the arrival of another vessel, also steaming down at full speed to be in at the death. She was the only other competitor in sight, and it was evidently to be a race between her and the *Guiding Hope* as to who should be there first.

'Open her out all you know!' howled Matthew down the engine-room voice-pipe. 'Let her rip, Jim!'

And Jim, who was perfectly well aware what was happening, did let her rip.

From eight thousand yards the distance rapidly dwindled to six, from six thousand to four, from four to a bare mile.

The great airship still struggled awkwardly to escape, the engines in the foremost gondola roaring out in sudden bursts as they strove to lift her, and the blast from her propellers ruffling the calm surface of the water like a cat's-paw of wind. Through his binoculars Matthew could soon see splashes in the water as things were jettisoned to lighten her. She was dying gamely, with the white, black-crossed ensign of the Imperial German Navy still hanging limply from her stern, and the huge, black Maltese Crosses and the number on her yellow belly showing clearly in the light of the risen sun. But all the while she was coming lower.

Boom! went the trawler's six-pounder, as, yawing a little to bring the weapon to bear, she summoned the airship to surrender.

The shell pitched across the Zeppelin's bows and burst in a little pillar of spray and a puff of smoke.

Boom! again—a little closer this time.

The roaring of the airship's engines suddenly ceased, and in an instant her stern fell until it touched the water. Next the after-gondola dipped into the sea, and the huge bulk of the monster, pivoting on the rear portion, settled slowly down until she floated on the surface with her bows cocked up and the foremost gondola hanging in mid-air.

Crash! went the *Guiding Hope's* gun again, and a ragged hole suddenly appeared in the flimsy fabric of the airship's bows as the projectile drove its way through without exploding.

Again the gun fired. Two more holes appeared, close to the first.

They were about to fire another round, when a man leant out of an opening in the foremost gondola, waving something white.

'*Kamerad!*' came his shout. '*Kamerad!*
Save, Englishman ; save ! '

Matthew smiled grimly. ' I 've half a mind
to *kamerad* the whole boilin' lot of you ! ' he
muttered to himself. ' I 'd scupper you all for
tuppence, damn murderin' pig-dogs ! '

Nevertheless, he stuck his head out of one
of the side-windows of the wheelhouse and
bellowed lustily for Moxon, the second hand.

' Charles,' he said when Moxon arrived, ' get
the boat out, an' go rescue them blighters.
Look out an' take pistols with you, an' if they
cuts up rusty or gives trouble, you knows what
to do. Them in the foremost bird-cage, the
one hangin' in the air, 'll have to jump overboard.'

' And suppose they won't come,' Charles
suggested.

' If they won't, tell 'em I 'll plug at 'em with
the six-pounder until I sets her afire. I
reckon they 'd sooner have wet shirts than
be frizzled in burnin' gas, or whatever it is
she 's filled with. But don't stand here
yarnin', Charles. Smart 's the word ! There 's
this other perisher comin', an' she 'll want to
have a say in things unless you look lively ! '

The ' other perisher ' was a trawler like the
Guiding Hope, and Matthew was anxious to
make certain of his prisoners before her arrival
on the scene. But she was coming up fast.

' And will you try towin' her home ? '
Moxon inquired as he lowered himself on
deck.

' May have a try at it after you 've taken

off them Huns. Nice li'l' job towin' a thing like that,' he added, eyeing the enormous bulk of the airship, and then glancing aft to compare it with his own tiny vessel. 'Nice li'l' thing to keep in the cowhouse at home to let the kid play with on Sundays!'

George, the helmsman, who was feeling rather pleased with himself, gave vent to his amusement in a chuckle. 'Don't you go forgettin', if there's any honour an' glory attached to this 'ere, that I saw 'er first, skipper,' he said. 'It was due to '——

'Go away, you old gargoyle!' laughed Matthew. 'Any silly fool could sight a thing like that. What are you out after—a V.C., or a medal for bravery?'

'No-o,' came the somewhat sheepish reply, for George was rather crestfallen at Matthew's indifference. 'I thought—leastways, I 'oped—as per'aps me likeness would come out in the *Mornin' Mirror.*'

The skipper stared at him as if his sanity were questionable, and then burst out into a roar of amusement.

'Yer see,' the would-be hero went on to explain in a throaty whisper, 'it's the wife. She's set 'er 'eart on bein' intervooed!'

'Interviewed?'

George nodded. 'Yus,' he said. 'Ever since Tom Witton, 'oo lives down our road, 'ad 'is missus intervooed an' 'is photo in the *Saturday Noos,* there's bin no 'oldin' my old woman. Tom Witton was blowed up by a mine, an' goes to 'ospital with 'is face all covered in bandages. " Gallant 'ero 'oo was six hours in the water afore bein' rescooed," they labels 'is likeness. Gallant 'ero !' with a snort of contempt. ' Bloomin' loonatic ! Any'ow, I 'll bet 'e didn't go swimmin' 'cos 'e liked it ! But they calls him a 'ero, all the same.'

' You 're jealous, George !'

' No, it ain't me, skipper. It 's the wife. I 'm a modest sort o' bloke.'

' You looks it, George,' murmured his commanding officer. ' There 's no holdin' the womenfolk, is there ? '

' No, skipper, there ain't ; an' that 's a fact !'

Matthew grinned. ' I can't waste time talkin' about 'em now,' he went on, putting his head out of the wheelhouse window.

' Hi, you sodgers !' in a roar like a bull of Bashan ; ' if you don't look lively with that boat, the other feller 'll nab them prisoners !'

This was the last thing the *Guiding Hope's* men wanted. They had never seen a real live Hun at close quarters, let alone a Zeppelin Hun ; and a Hun of any species was well worth striving for, if only as a curio. So in less than five minutes, by which time the rival trawler had come within half a mile, the boat was half-way across to the Zeppelin.

Presently, when she was close alongside, the Germans could be seen throwing themselves into the sea and swimming towards her. One by one they were hauled into safety, and having rescued seventeen, the boat, very deep in the water, started to pull back.

'Got the lot?' asked Matthew as she came close.

'Two officers and fifteen men!' Moxon shouted back.

'Get 'em on board quick!' the skipper ordered.

The dripping prisoners clambered on board; while Matthew, leaving the wheelhouse, went on deck to interview a tall, fair-haired officer wearing the stripes of an *oberleutnant* of the Imperial German Navy.

'Are you the capten of her?' he inquired gruffly.

'I am,' the German answered surlily, but in excellent English. 'What of it?'

'Are all your men here?'

'Two are left.'

'Why didn't they come?'

'They do their duty,' said the foreigner, drawing himself up. 'We cast lots as to who shall remain. It falls to them.' He shrugged his shoulders.

'But why'——

Matthew's question was cut short by the crash of an explosion. He looked round, to see the foremost gondola of the airship enveloped in a cloud of grayish smoke, and the water all around splashed with falling wreckage. Then, when the pall cleared away, the gondola hung in shreds, and they could see a flickering tongue of vivid blue flame creeping slowly round the belly of the monster.

The German, biting his lips, watched it anxiously. 'Ah, she burns!' he said at last, as the flame grew. 'That was why the men remained. You cannot take her now!'

He brought his hand to his head in a salute; and his men, clicking their heels, followed his example.

In less than half-a-minute the blue twinkle of fire blazed out suddenly into scarlet. Next a great gout of vivid orange, and almost immediately the entire forepart of the great thing became enveloped in a sheet of brilliant flame. Then a cloud of thick black smoke burst out, as the fire, roaring like a blast-furnace, spread rapidly. The blunt bows of the airship dipped towards the water until the very sea seemed ablaze and smoking.

The heat was overpowering, and the *Guiding Hope*, far too close to find it pleasant, took her boat hastily in tow and steamed off. But before she had travelled even half a mile the end came.

There was a hissing, sizzling sound as fire and water came into contact. Wreathing eddies of white steam filtered fantastically through the pall of smoke. The blaze flickered, and then died sullenly away; while the dark smoke-cloud trailed languidly to leeward along the surface in a travelling curtain. Then, when the smoke had finally disappeared from the spot where the airship had rested, not a vestige of her enormous bulk could be seen— nothing but a long patch of blackened sea littered with charred débris, and overhung by a thin film of vapour.

The *Guiding Hope* approached the place

and circled through it, stopping a while to pick up a piece of charred fabric, a portion of one of the gondolas, a few personal belongings of the crew, and other relics. She then dropped buoys to mark the position, and, with a triumphant hoot on her whistle, her wireless chattering, and her men offering dry clothing, cocoa, food, and cigarettes to their rather astonished prisoners, steamed merrily back towards her base.

'I can't understand them fellers at all,' said the second hand, arriving in the wheelhouse a few minutes later with smiles all over his face.

'What's up with 'em?' Matthew asked.

'I was talkin' just now to one of 'em who knows a bit of English, an' he asks me quite serious what time he an' all his mates was goin' to be shot!'

'Shot!' ejaculated the skipper. 'Why?'

Moxon laughed. 'That's what I asks him,' he said, 'an' he tells me their officers fills 'em all up with a yarn that we never takes prisoners home alive. We either shoots 'em in the water, flings 'em overboard, or else poisons 'em!'*

* As an example of a rather prevalent idea among German seamen as to how the British Navy treats its prisoners, it may be mentioned that after the action in the Heligoland Bight in August 1914, some Germans on board a British destroyer refused to drink cocoa offered to them by their rescuers. It was not until one of our men drank from the same bowl that they could be prevailed upon to touch it. Their officers, they said, had told them to beware of poisoned food in the event of their being made prisoners. There have been many other incidents of a similar nature, some occurring even during the fourth year of the war.

German seamen rescued at sea generally show the profoundest

' And what did you tell him, Charles ? '

' I says it 's all a pack o' lies; but I could see he didn't believe a word I said, an' still thinks he 's goin' to be done in ! '

' 'Stead of which we pulls 'em out of the water, treats 'em like gents, an' gives 'em comfortable quarters an' good food,' said Matthew. ' I 'm a soft-hearted sort o' chap meself,' he went on, ' but I reckons there 's some of 'em ought never to be rescued.'

' Perhaps there is,' Moxon agreed.

.   .   .   .

' Zeppelins visited the eastern counties on the night of the 19th–20th,' ran the official *communiqué*. ' The raiders were heavily engaged and turned back by our defending aeroplanes and anti - aircraft batteries. Bombs were dropped in various localities, but no damage of military importance was done. One airship, flying low in a damaged condition, jettisoned her cargo of bombs in an outlying district. A cottage was unfortunately struck, and the inmates, a woman and a child, were killed. These are the only casualties reported up to the present. This same airship subsequently came down in the sea, and most of

gratitude, but some astonishment, at being picked up and humanely treated, as if they had been taught to expect the very opposite. On one fairly recent occasion I was personally thanked by an English-speaking petty officer, with tears in his eyes, for sparing his life, and he expressed considerable surprise at not having been fired at in the water with a machine-gun.

It is only fair to add that, in the greater number of cases, British survivors rescued by the enemy during the battle of Jutland were treated with kindness and consideration on board the German ships.

her crew were rescued by one of our vessels. Another was brought down in flames and totally destroyed.'

Altogether the tone of the message was distinctly encouraging, for the raid had been a dismal failure.

But it completely knocked the bottom out of Matthew Conolly's life, for by some ghastly freak of fortune the cottage on which the bomb had fallen happened to be his.

IV.

Towards eight o'clock in the morning the thick fog which had prevailed throughout the night began slowly to evaporate in the rays of the strengthening sun. The grayish curtain, which had reduced the visibility to a few hundred yards, gradually dispersed and broke away in wreathing eddies of smoky vapour, until, an hour later, the weather settled down into that unsatisfactory, indeterminate state, neither foggy nor really clear, which is so prevalent during summer in the southern areas of the North Sea.

The sky overhead was intensely blue, but the mist hung close to the surface in low-lying, isolated patches like cotton-wool. At one moment the visibility might be four or five miles, while the next the sea became shrouded in haze until the horizon was a bare ten cables distant. It was one of those sultry mornings with no breath of wind to cool the atmosphere or to dissipate the mist. There was an oppressive, electrical feeling in the air as if a thunderstorm were approaching, and a hint of coming trouble in the long, glassy swell rolling in from the south-westward.

Two men of the *Guiding Hope*, their morning meal finished and the prospect of an idle forenoon before them, gravitated instinctively to the shade of the bulwarks, there to sit on deck smoking their pipes preparatory to relapsing into slumber.

'This weather fair licks creation!' grunted a jersey-clad, sea-booted little man with earrings, an orange muffler, and little beads of perspiration showing on his fat, red face. 'Onnatural, I calls it.'

'Some folk is never satisfied,' his companion sleepily observed. 'When it's cold they 'ollers, and when it's 'ot they shouts. Lord only knows what some o' you fellers do want!'

'Heat's a dangerous thing in our family,' the first speaker explained. 'Seems to run in the blood, like. I once had a naunt who died o' aperplexy on an August Bank Holiday, and when the doctor see'd her he—— 'Strewth! Look at our Moll!' he broke off, pointing to the trawler's black-and-white cat, who, with her fur on end, her tail waving in the air, and her head moving from side to side, was padding mincingly up and down, to and fro, like a caged tiger.

'She's bin goin' on like that all the mornin',' said the other, watching the animal. 'Why can't she go to sleep in the day-time like any or'nary Christian cat? What's come over 'er?'

'It's a nomen, Jim,' said the superstitous gentleman with the apoplectic aunt.

'An 'ow much, Bill?'

'Omen—a sign,' came the answer. 'Them animals knows more 'n we humans does, and when they carries on like that, it means somethin' 's goin' to 'appen.—Here, Moll,' he cried, making a sound with his lips and stretching out a hand in a tentative caress as the creature came towards him; 'what's ailin' you, old gel?'

The animal glanced at him with her baleful yellow eyes blazing. Then, baring her teeth, she spat aggressively, and lashed out with a paw armed with its row of unsheathed claws, immediately to spring sideways, out of reach of possible retaliation.

'Well, I be damned in heaps!' ejaculated the astonished Bill, gazing at the blood slowly oozing from the parallel scores down the back of his sunburnt hand. 'She's been and gone and scratched me, the little devil! Never know'd her do that afore, and me her best friend, too.'

'You said somethin' was goin' to 'appen, Bill,' guffawed his mate. 'Strikes me you was right.'

'Right! The bloomin' cat's gone clean daft, anyhow. And when a cat goes daft like that, somethin' always 'appens! You see if it don't.'

But Jim, a disbeliever in omens and portents, merely shook his head and laughed.

The *Guiding Hope* was out at sea acting as

shepherd and watch-dog to a number of fishing-trawlers engaged upon their lawful business of adding to the nation's food-supply, and at intervals throughout the forenoon the blurred shapes of her little flock, scattered over an area of a few miles, alternately came into view and disappeared with the rising and the thickening of the mist.

There was no particular cause for anxiety, as no hostile vessels had visited the locality for weeks and months. Nevertheless, it behoved the watchers to keep a sharp look-out, since Fritz, to give him his due, was a persistent sort of fellow, with a knack of appearing when he was least expected, and well the 'Guiding Hopes' knew it. But they rather liked their job, all the same. They had their trawl on board, and were occasionally permitted to while away the weary hours by doing a little fishing on their own account, which reminded them of the happier days of peace. Moreover, it was always a welcome change from the ordinary humdrum monotony of patrolling an area of sea, sometimes with hardly another vessel in sight. There they felt terribly lonely; but here, on the fishing-grounds, they were surrounded by their friends. Numbers invariably breed a sense of security.

The day wore on, and brought no appreciable change in the weather. It was precisely at seven minutes past four in the afternoon, when the trawler was enveloped in a slowly drifting bank of mist, rather thicker than usual, that there came the sudden crash of a gun from the northward. It seemed quite close at hand, and Matthew, who had turned the watch over to Moxon, and had just gone below to his tea, returned immediately to the wheelhouse.

Two more shattering reports shook the air as, without waiting to issue any orders, he pushed the helmsman aside, wrenched the wheel hard over, and jangled the engine-room telegraph to full speed.

'Get the gun manned!' he muttered hastily to the second hand. 'Yon may be anything. Sounds like big guns!'

The men themselves needed no encouragement, for already the sound of guns had brought the members of the watch below clambering out of the forecastle in all stages of deshabille to rush to their action stations.

Bur-o-o-o-p! b-o-o-m! again, followed immediately by the duller thudding explosion of a bursting shell, and a shrill screeching somewhere overhead as a projectile, striking the water, ricochetted through the mist without bursting.

Then came the sharper crack of a lighter gun giving tongue, and in an instant the din became deafening, an ear-splitting medley in which the deep, booming reports of heavy artillery, mingling with the shriller crashes of the smaller weapon, reverberated through the mist in an unceasing volume of sound. They—whoever 'they' might be—were at it hammer and tongs, firing as fast as they could slam home the projectiles and the cartridges.

Once more that demoniacal whistle burst out

in the air as a shell drove overhead. Next a heavy splash, and a geyser of white spray leapt into the air a bare seventy yards on the *Guiding Hope's* starboard beam. The chance shell burst with a puff of black smoke, and with a buzz and an angry humming like a swarm of enraged bees, a drove of splinters came hurtling through the air. Something struck the trawler's funnel with a clang like a blow from a sledge-hammer.

Matthew felt the perspiration rolling down his face. It was the uncertainty and the lack of knowledge as to what was in progress that agitated him. The fact that his own life might presently be in danger did not disturb him in the slightest. Indeed, his own personal safety and that of his men and his ship hardly even entered his mind. He was so inured to danger in all its many shapes that fear did not trouble him, and his principal feelings were those of intense excitement and an ardent anxiety to know what was happening. Moreover, his duty lay clearly before him, and it was very simple. He had to get to the scene of action as fast as steam and his own good sense could carry him. Nothing else mattered for the present ; and when he got there—well, there was no knowing what might happen, so why consider it ?

Life, after all, was nothing that really signified. To him, since the death of his wife and only child, it had become a hopeless, dreary purgatory, with nothing to make it worth while. It was a matter of indifference whether he lived or died. There was nobody dependent on his efforts, not a soul in the world to mourn his loss; and if the cold, gray North Sea did gather him into her arms for safe keeping until the Day of Judgment, he would only be going the way of many other good men before him.

If only the mist would clear away and vouchsafe him one fleeting glimpse of the fight to allow him to make up his mind!

But the haze seemed thicker than ever, and the visibility had dwindled to a bare quarter of a mile.

If only the ship could steam a little faster! But already she was pounding along at her best speed.

And still the thudding of those fiendish guns continued, louder and louder, until the very air trembled to the discharges. The suspense became maddening; for even now, somewhere fairly close at hand in the mist, men were fighting for their lives, fighting against he knew not what. His countrymen were dying—mangled or blasted to pieces by high-explosive shell, battling in the water against an inevitable death. Men were dying —dying by slow degrees—and he was not there to succour them.

Suddenly, as if by magic, the tumult of the guns ceased, the thunder of their reports being superseded by the shrill, roaring whistle of escaping steam.

The mist, thinning appreciably, trailed aside to leave an ever-widening lane of clear water ahead of the *Guiding Hope*. It grew broader and broader as Matthew, half-beside himself with pent-up excitement, watched it with anxious eyes. Then, at a spot about eight hundred yards distant, the woolly vapour on the edge of the fog-bank seemed to darken, and gradually, for all the world like a picture on the screen at a magic-lantern display, the familiar shape of a fishing-trawler slid slowly into view.

But she was not an ordinary-looking trawler. Her bows were cocked up at an absurd angle until her curved forefoot was out of the water, while her overhanging stern touched the sea as, with a heavy list to starboard, she rolled sluggishly to the swell. Her funnel had disappeared, and a volume of black smoke, mingled with a white cloud of high-pressure steam from some severed pipe, ascended lazily in the air. She was ablaze amidships, and on the water-line a gaping orifice, which dipped now and then into the sea as she swung drunkenly from side to side, showed where an exploding shell had done its evil work. There were many other perforations and gashes in the hull; while the stern and the wheelhouse, or what could be seen of them for smoke and dancing flame, seemed mangled and battered into a tangle of twisted, distorted steelwork. There were no signs of life on board. Not a man appeared as the *Guiding Hope* approached.

Then, just beyond and a little to one side of the wreck, something else drifted slowly

into view—something dark and long, like a
streak on the water, with a curious hump in
the middle. And in an instant Matthew,
with a prayer in his heart, had headed his
ship straight in that direction. There was no
mistaking what it was—a German submarine,
one of the largest underwater craft he had
ever seen.

She lay stopped on the surface perhaps
seven hundred yards off, and as she came into

clear view, men on her low hull could be
seen helping swimmers from the water and
dragging them on board. She carried a large
gun on each side of the conning-tower, and
seeing that the crews were not standing by
their weapons, the skipper prayed and hoped
that he might be able to approach her
unawares. But he knew in his heart that he
had little chance of doing so. If he could see
her, she, also, could see his ship; while the full

speed of the *Guiding Hope* was no more than a bare ten knots. It would take his vessel something like two minutes to cover the distance which separated her from her enemy. Two minutes—and at any moment the submarine might open fire with those two 4.1's of hers. It might have been two hours, for all the difference it made. Whatever happened, the *Guiding Hope* seemed doomed. Nothing short of a miracle could save her.

Out of the corner of his eye Matthew saw the battered trawler rear her bows skywards, and founder stern first with a convulsive, almost human, wriggle. Then the submarine's crew seemed suddenly conscious of the *Guiding Hope's* presence, for an officer on the conning-tower waved an arm and shouted, and parties of men rushed to the guns.

But still Matthew held his course, hoping against hope that with his smaller and more nimble craft he might yet be able to ram before the submarine could gather headway and escape. Moreover, the bows of the *Guiding Hope* offered a smaller target than her broadside, though it meant that the six-pounder, mounted amidships abaft the funnel, could not be brought to bear.

Six hundred and fifty yards—six hundred—five seventy-five.

Then came a swirl from the submarine's stern, as, leaving some of the swimmers still struggling in the water, her propellers revolved and she started to move slowly ahead. Almost at once followed an orange flash and the report from one of her weapons, accompanied by the terrifying screech of the shell as it passed close alongside and plumped into the sea a short distance astern.

Another spurt of flame and a roar ; but this time a crash, a violent shudder, a shower of splinters and upflung débris, and a wave of acrid picric smoke drifting in through the wheelhouse window warned Matthew that the ship had been hit somewhere forward.

Another report, another, and yet another, until they merged into a regular, deafening roar.

Mingled with the din of the firing came the eerie screeching of projectiles tearing through the air, the booming thud of their explosion, the whirring, humming, and buzzing of splinters, and an infernal clanging and battering when they struck, as if all the pneumatic riveters in the world were busily at work on the *Guiding Hope's* hull. Crash succeeded crash. The ship quivered and shook, while the forepart was ablaze from end to end, until the flames licked in through the wheelhouse windows, and the place became filled with the sickening reek of explosives, smoke, and the bitter fumes of burning paint, which made Matthew cough and splutter for breath.

Abandoning his intention of ramming as quite useless, as indeed it was, the skipper swung his ship round to bring his gun to bear. It was the only possible thing to do, in the hope that a lucky shell from the six-pounder might disable the enemy or cause him to dive.

But what chance had their single puny weapon against the two larger guns of their opponent?

At the back of his mind Matthew was perfectly well aware that his ship was fighting her last battle. He realised that he and his men were staring death in the face. The possibility of escape never entered his head—escape, indeed, was out of the question—and in the brief intervals between the reports of the hostile guns he heard the bark of his own little weapon as his men fell to work. And hopeless though the situation was, the sound cheered him.

Through the rifts in the surrounding smoke-haze he could still catch momentary glimpses of the long, wicked-looking shape of the submarine, with the vicious tongues of flame darting from her guns. An occasional plume of spray somewhere near her, moreover, showed that the six-pounder was making tolerably good practice, though it must have been well-nigh impossible for the gun-layer to see what he was firing at.

But the *Guiding Hope* had been struck repeatedly, and her speed, owing to some injury in the engine-room, had dwindled to a mere crawl. There was a crash and a gout of blinding, golden flame from aft, and the funnel, struck at the base, tottered drunkenly and fell to the deck in a smoking ruin. A wave of hot smoke came pouring into the wheelhouse, one corner of which had been opened to the sky. The next moment another shell burst

on deck outside, and instantly the sides and
the floor became perforated in a hundred
places by slivers of flying steel. The helmsman, his face deathly white, clapped his hand
to his side with the blood streaming from
between his fingers. He opened his mouth to
speak, but no sounds came ; and swaying for a
moment, he slid to the deck and rolled over,
twitching horribly.

Matthew, pulling him aside, jumped to the
wheel; while the wounded man, finding his
voice, screamed in a shrill falsetto and clutched
him round the ankles.

'Let go!' the skipper shouted, kicking
himself free with all his might. 'Let go,
can't you?'

The poor wretch relapsed into a sitting
posture, with his back against the bulkhead.
His head fell forward on his chest, and rolling
over, he lay quite still.

The helm was useless, as the trawler had
been brought to a standstill. Matthew was
wounded, too, for he could feel a dull, burning
pain in his left shoulder. He tried to raise
the arm, but the movement made him wince
with pain, and looking down, he saw with
some astonishment that a trickle of blood was
flowing down his arm and dribbling from his
fingers to the floor. He felt dizzy and faint.
His knees seemed suddenly to be made of
jelly.

An unrecognisable, ragged apparition, with
blackened face, blood pouring from a jagged
cut across the forehead, and the fingers of its

right hand pulped and bloody, crawled into the wheelhouse.

'Skipper!' it gasped hoarsely—'skipper! all the gun's crew is killed! Ship's afire aft! Can't stop it!'

Even as the words were spoken there came another roar and a flash as a shell burst outside, and a splinter, taking Moxon in the side, struck him to the deck.

'God!' Matthew whispered stupidly. 'Good God! Who'd 'a' thought it?'

He started to leave the wheelhouse with the intention of going on deck to see what could be done to cope with the fire, but hardly had he emerged when there came another burst of flame.

He was picked up and hurled through space. He felt himself falling, falling . . . but never felt the shock of landing, for in that brief instant, wounded again in the neck and the body, Matthew had become unconscious.

It may have been five minutes before he recovered his senses, or perhaps twenty-five, but when he opened his eyes again the firing had ceased.

He found himself lying close to the huddled, lifeless body of the second hand. He was bruised, nearly numb with pain, and bleeding cruelly, but his brain was still active. The ship had heeled over to an impossible angle, and he could tell from her sluggish rolling that her end was not far distant. The fire aft seemed to have burnt itself out, though wisps of steam and smoke and a few tongues of flame still flickered lazily in the air. The afterpart of the ship resembled a heap of discarded scrap-steel; the woodwork was blackened and splintered fantastically; while the six-pounder had been knocked over backwards, and lay with its muzzle pointing forlornly in the air, the bodies of its crew lying in contorted attitudes around it. Nobody stirred. Not a soul but himself seemed to be left alive.

But he was even yet capable of clear thought. The instinct of caution still possessed him, and he felt a desperate curiosity to see what had become of the submarine. He knew better than to draw a burst of fire by raising his head into view. Instead of that, he started to crawl painfully along the deck on his hands and knees, under the shelter of the bulwarks, towards a gaping, ragged gash caused by a shell. The effort hurt him cruelly, but reaching the hole and peering cautiously out, he saw what he wanted to see.

The submarine was lying motionless within a couple of hundred yards, basking on the surface like some great whale. The men were still congregated round the guns, the muzzles of which pointed in the trawler's direction; while an officer on the conning-tower was examining the wreck through a pair of binoculars.

Withdrawing his head and looking aft, Matthew saw the trawler's White Ensign, torn and sadly bedraggled, flapping from the ensign-staff in the stern. He felt glad it was there—glad that the *Guiding Hope* had never surrendered, and that she would go to the bottom with her colours flying. And from the flag his gaze wandered down to two large cylindrical objects secured to sloping trays on the trawler's counter.

'God!' he gasped, as an idea struck him in a flash.

He took another cautious look at the submarine, and saw that the officer had put down his glasses and was talking to a subordinate. Then, pointing in the *Guiding Hope's* direction, the officer seemed to make up his mind, for a flutter of water appeared at the vessel's stern, and she started to move slowly towards the trawler.

Matthew, without waiting for a moment, drew his heavy sailor's knife and began to crawl aft along the deck. His left arm hung limp and useless, he left a trail of blood behind him, and every movement was an agony; but still he crawled. Foot by foot he advanced, resting every now and then to gather strength.

Presently he abandoned his knife in favour of a short bar of steel which he found lying on deck. He gripped it in his right hand, and moved on. At last, after what seemed an eternity, breathless and weak with pain, he found himself crouching under the trawler's counter with those cylinders above him and within easy reach. And those cylinders contained explosive charges especially designed for destroying submarines. Explosive charges !

and even now a German submarine was coming alongside to investigate—perhaps to capture that precious ensign, or to search the ship for any secret books or orders which might be of value. Matthew almost laughed aloud at the trap she was blindly sailing into.

He could hear the wash of water and the sound of guttural voices. The voices came closer and closer. He nerved his battered body for its final effort.

There came a jar as something rubbed along the trawler's side. The submarine had arrived, and at any moment a man might leap on board and frustrate his intention. It was now or never.

Raising himself to his tottering feet, he sprang at the cylinders in the stern and struck blindly, wildly, at their securing-slips. Some one shouted, a pistol flashed close at hand, but he struck again and again. One of the slips parted, and the first cylinder fell into the water with a heavy splash.

Yells broke out from the German craft alongside, and he heard a bullet go whistling past his head. He could see a man standing on her low bow within a few feet of him with his smoking weapon pointed full at his face. But he did not heed it. He struck again and again. The second cylinder went overboard with a plop.

The skipper suddenly had the feeling as if a red-hot iron had penetrated his side, and in the same instant he caught sight of an automatic pistol in the hand of the officer on the submarine's conning-tower spurting flame as it was emptied towards him. He felt another bullet strike him somewhere in the neck, but he was past caring what happened, and stood there streaming with blood, blackened, and spent, holding on to the bulwarks.

'Got you, you swine!' he suddenly roared in an ecstasy of mad excitement, hurling his only weapon, the bar in his hand, full at a man in the submarine who was preparing to spring on board.

The bar caught the German in the chest and knocked him overboard, and Matthew laughed in his mad glee.

'You're all going to hell quick!' he shouted again, taunting them.

A bullet hit him in the head, and his legs crumpled beneath him, but even as he dropped there came the thudding roar of an explosion under water . . . and yet another. A dome-shaped mass of white water rose at the *Guiding Hope's* stern and broke into spray. The little ship was literally lifted in the air . . . but Matthew knew nought of it all. He was dead.

The haze rolled aside.

.   .   .   .   .   .

It was a little fishing-trawler which brought the news home—a rusty little trawler with spray-whitened funnels, fresh from the fishing-grounds of the North Sea.

Her men told the tale of two separate and distinct encounters with a submarine, and of how one of their little fishing-fleet was missing.

But they also told the story of two thundering explosions, of how the mist lifted, and how, with their own eyes, they saw the *Guiding Hope* go down stern first with her ensign still flying.

Close beside her when she took her final plunge was another vessel, a huge, gray-painted submarine with her bow dipped deep in the water and her pointed stern reared in the air until rudder and propeller were clearly visible. Her crew were lined up on her sloping deck, and shouted for help as the trawler approached. Even as the crew of the British vessel looked on, the U-boat was slowly sinking. Then the Germans flung themselves into the water, while their vessel, pointing her stern skywards like a huge spear-head, vanished for ever to the depths in a little splutter of spray and an up-heaval of bubbles.

Matthew had done his work well.

They picked up several wounded Englishmen from the first trawler sunk, and many unwounded Germans, including two officers, whom they made prisoners. But of anybody belonging to the *Guiding Hope* there was no trace, though they searched the wreckage-strewn area for over an hour.

So somewhere in the gray depths of the North Sea lies all that was mortal of Matthew Conolly and his men. Their sepulchre is the shell-battered hull of their own little ship, their tombstones the foaming white-caps. Their epitaph is written across the sky in the trail of smoke from some passing vessel; while the gulls, wheeling and dipping, scream their ceaseless dirge overhead.

But the memories of those men will ever be green in the hearts of those who knew and loved them—and Matthew Conolly was my friend.

CHAPTER X.

A LITTLE DROP O' LEAF.

I.

THE barometer had fallen with a thump the previous day, and now, with the short winter afternoon fast drawing to a close, the weather was as dirty as it possibly could be. A piercing north-easterly gale, with occasional snow-flurries and showers of sleet, howled and shrieked across the harbour until the usually sheltered anchorage was torn and whipped into fury. The tide running against the wind had raised a curling, perpendicular lop of a sea which made boatwork inadvisable, if not positively dangerous, and every ship in the harbour had hoisted her boats and held no communication with the shore.

Masses of flying spindrift, cut from the surface as if with a gigantic sickle, went hurtling to leeward across the tumbling, white-gray water; while overhead, in the darkening sky, heavy, leaden-looking bunches of cloud, streaked with the white wisps of mares' tails, and torn and fretted by the wind, came sailing rapidly down from windward on the wings of the gale.

The destroyers, tugging and straining at their buoys, all had steam up and anchors ready for letting go, lest, by some unfortunate chance, their moorings should part and they

should find themselves adrift and helpless.
Such things have been known to happen for
want of the necessary precautions. Even as
it was, the spray came flying in sheets across
their low decks when the tide swung them
across the sea and the wind.

The *Triptolemus* happened to be lying close
to the *Mariner*, and I, having been ashore
earlier in the afternoon with Dick, the Sealyham, had hastened back when the weather
got worse. But even so, my own ship had
already hoisted her boats, and I only just
succeeded in catching the *Mariner's* motor-
boat, which happened to be waiting at the
jetty. So now, through no fault of my own,
I was weather-bound on board that hospitable
vessel. I knew her officers of old, and could
not have wished for better company.

Dówn below everything was snug and
warm, and in the wardroom, Peter Wooten,
her commanding officer, stood with his back
to the blazing stove. 'Looks as if you'd have
to spend the night here,' he said to me,
glancing out of a tightly closed scuttle as
a particularly heavy squall struck the ship.
'Weather's getting worse every minute.
Thank Heaven we're not at sea!'

'Amen to that, sir,' murmured the first-
lieutenant, engrossed in *La Vie Parisienne*
in the depths of an arm-chair. 'Lord!
wouldn't our little "Ikey" be sick?'

'Not so much of your "Ikey," Number One,'
growled Thompson, the engineer-lieutenant-
commander, who rather resented a nickname

which he really did not deserve. 'Anyhow,' he added with a yawn, 'I'd far sooner be an Israelite than a Glasgow Highlander!'

M'Donald, the first-lieutenant, proud of his nationality, deposited his paper in a place of safety, rose to his feet, buttoned his coat, and, without saying another word, fell upon the engineer.

'Scrap! Scrap!' howled the sub. joyfully, as the combatants, locked in each other's arms, fell violently on to the settee in close proximity to the sleeping Sealyham. 'Up and at 'em!'

He hurled himself from his chair and into the fray without quite knowing or caring which side he proposed to fight on; while Dick, forgetting his manners, and equally excited, pranced eagerly round on the outskirts of the battle, barking furiously and snapping playfully at anything within reach.

'Behave yourselves, you devils!' laughed Wooten, hurling a cushion into the midst of the fight, and jumping aside to avoid a waving leg. 'Play light, children. Play light!'

For some moments the 'children,' struggling and panting heavily, with the engineer underneath, the first lieutenant above him, and the sub. on top of the lot, fought lustily on the settee in a maze of whirling arms and legs. Then Dick, seizing his opportunity, dashed in and got his jaws to work.

'Ow!' yelled the first lieutenant. 'The little brute's got me by the breeches! Let go, you chaps! He's tearing 'em to bits!'

The struggle terminated abruptly, and the

combatants, disentangling themselves, rose to their feet, flushed, breathless, and laughing.

'Serve you jolly well right, Number One,' gasped Thompson, adjusting his torn collar. 'Even Dick knows you for a heathen!'

M'Donald laughed good-humouredly. 'All right, Ikey dear,' he panted, rather red about the face. 'You got the worst of it, anyhow.'

'Did I?' guffawed the engineer. 'Look at your breeks.'

The Sealyham's teeth were sharp, and he had torn one leg of the first lieutenant's trousers almost to the knee.

'Well, I'll be jiggered!' he exclaimed, examining the damage with a rueful expression. 'They're my second-best pair!'

Everybody laughed; while Dick, slobbering profusely, wagged his tail and grinned in his usual doggish way. 'After all,' he seemed to be saying, 'I may be a guest; but if my superior officers amuse themselves by pretending to fight, why shouldn't I join in?'

Why not, indeed?

On the mess-deck forward the men comported themselves with rather more dignity. There was a certain amount of noise, it is true, for many of them were talking at the top of their voices; a gramophone was raucously grinding out 'Dixie;' and in the far corner the members of a very much home-made orchestra, composed of one man with a mouth-organ and another with a penny whistle, were trying hard to get their respective instruments to synchronise in time and tune. Another man helped them with an occasional tympanic accompaniment beaten out on the bottom of a tin mess-kettle, and his efforts, combined with those of the gentleman with the whistle, who could not play a little bit, were penetrating, to say the least of it.

Another A.B. was busily embroidering a cushion-cover in Berlin wool on canvas. It was quite a work of art, and included a crown, a portrait of His Majesty surrounded with a wreath of roses, thistles, shamrocks, and leeks in their proper colouring, the flags of all the Allies, and the words 'RULE BRITANNIA' in gold, all on on a ground of vivid emerald-green. 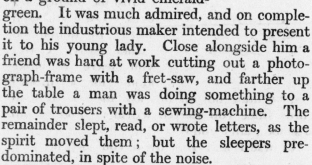 It was much admired, and on completion the industrious maker intended to present it to his young lady. Close alongside him a friend was hard at work cutting out a photograph-frame with a fret-saw, and farther up the table a man was doing something to a pair of trousers with a sewing-machine. The remainder slept, read, or wrote letters, as the spirit moved them; but the sleepers predominated, in spite of the noise.

At the foremost table on the starboard side sat Leading Seaman Joshua Billings and William Martin, A.B. Billings, a short, stout, red-faced fellow, with a voice like an asthmatic corn-crake, was pretending to read a yellow-backed magazine. In reality, he had just consumed a very satisfactory tea, and was feeling extremely replete and comfortable—so replete, in fact, that his head nodded, and the printed pages danced before his half-closed eyes.

Martin, generally known as 'Pincher,' was sprawling with his elbows on the white wooden table, gazing every now and then at the ceiling for inspiration, for he was endeavouring to write a letter. Pincher was a smaller man than his neighbour, lightly built and rather thin, but his clear complexion and eyes, and alert manner and movements, showed that he enjoyed the best of health.

''Ere, Josh,' he asked, sucking the end of his pen, and nudging his burly friend in the

ribs, ''ow d'you spell affectionate?'

Joshua opened his eyes. ''Ow d'you spell wot?' he demanded rather testily. 'Carn't you leave a bloke alone for a minit? You've done nothin' but ask me 'ow to spell words since you started writin'! You've bin to school, ain't you?'

'Course I 'as.   But 'ow d'you spell it?'

'Spell wot?'

'Affectionate.'

Billings thought for a moment: 'A F F E X-U N, affection—A T E, ain't it, fat-head?'

Pincher wrote it down and stared at it doubtfully. 'Sounds all right,' he said, scratching his head. 'Don't look right, some'ow.'

'Good enuf, ain't it? 'Oo are you writin' to, any'ow?'

''Oo do you think?'

'Your Hemmeline?'

'Course. 'Oo else d' you think?'

'I dunno wot other gals you writes to, I 'm sure,' said Joshua. ''Ere, let 's 'ave a look at it?' He held out a hand.

Pincher snatched his precious letter away.

'No,' he said; 'it 's private.'

The leading seaman snorted. 'Privit! 'Ow can it be? Now, look 'ere, me son; you don't go 'avin' no secrets from me, mind.'

'Oh, don't I?'

'No, you bloomin' well don't. Your gal Hemmeline—your missus, that is—is my missus's daughter by 'er first 'usband, ain't she?'

'Yes.'

'An' as your missus's ma—your ma-in-law, that is—is my missus, I 'm your bloomin' pa-in-law, ain't I?'

Pincher laughed. 'I dunno so much about that,' he observed.

'Course I is,' Joshua pointed out; 'an' seein' as 'ow I 'm your pa-in-law, I 'm the bloke wot 's responsible for you. Therefore you 've gotter obey wot I says, same as if I was your proper farther; an' when I arsks you civil to show me wot you wrote, you becomes 'ongrateful, an' says you won't. All right, then,' he went on, waving a podgy hand. 'All right, 'ave it your own way; but don't come cryin' an' 'owlin' round my neck when you 're

in trouble, that's all. Base ingratitood's
wot I calls it, arter all I done for you!'

'All you done for me,' Martin chuckled.
'I likes that. 'Oo was it 'oo borrowed 'arf-a-
dollar orf me last pay-day, an' ain't returned
it? 'Oo is it 'oo arsks me for 'bacca an'
matches, an' says 'e ain't got none of 'is own,
eh? 'Oo is it? I know it's me poor old pa-
in-law. 'Is name is Josh Billings.'

Joshua, seeing that the war was being
carried into his own territory, grunted in
disgust, and relapsed into silence. Within
five minutes, breathing stertorously, he was
fast asleep.

Pincher, smiling to himself, completed his
letter with two rows of crosses, stamped and
addressed the envelope, and leaving it open,
placed it in the letter-box. It, with many
others, would presently be read and passed by
the unfortunate officer whose duty it was to
censor all the private correspondence leaving
the ship, and even the most intimate letters to
wives and sweethearts were not exempt from
his rigid scrutiny.

Two minutes later, however, another diver-
sion was caused by the sudden arrival on the
mess-deck of a breathless, red-faced signalman, whose oilskins dripped with wet.

''Ullo, Buntin'!' somebody asked appre-
hensively, eyeing the signal-pad in the new-
comer's hand. 'What's the racket now?'

'I knows,' said another man glumly. 'We
raises steam fur full speed with the utmost
despatch, an' goes to sea to 'unt Fritzes.

Lawd,' he added, 'wot a night to be out on th' rollin' waves!'

The signalman smiled blandly. 'Any o' you blokes fancy a drop o' leaf?' he inquired, ignoring his questioners.

'Leaf! 'Oo said leaf?' grunted Billings, waking up at the mere mention of the word. 'Garn! We 'aven't 'ad no leaf for months, an' months, an' months, as th' song says, an' ain't likely to, neither!'

'All right, then,' said Bunting. 'Listen to this signal just come through: "Raise steam by seven o'clock in the mornin'. *Mariner* will proceed to refit at . . . Orders are being sent." How's that for a bit of all right?'

'Sure you ain't spinnin' yarns?' Pincher asked incredulously.

'Of course I'm ruddy well not! If you likes to go down to the wardroom you'll see th' skipper, an' the sub-lootenant, an' th' engineer orficer, an' all the rest of 'em dancin' ring-a-ring-o'-roses round th' table. Here,' he added, thrusting the pad into Martin's hand, 'read the bloomin' signal for yourself!'

Pincher read, and was convinced.

'It's orl right, blokes,' he observed, smiling happily. 'There ain't no 'anky-panky about it. 'Strewth!' he added. 'To-day's the twenty-second o' December, an' one watch'll be 'ome for Christmas Day, an' th' other for th' Noo Year.'

''Ear, 'ear!' from the delighted Billings; while a chorus of cheers, yells, and cat-calls came from the others.

The sleepers awoke, and for the next half-hour the *Mariner's* mess-deck was in a state of howling pandemonium.

So also was the wardroom, for we spent the evening in celebration. Leave was a thing people did not often get; while leave at Christmas, the one time of the year when everybody wanted to be at home, had been unknown to most of them since 1913.

They made a night of it, and it was not until past midnight, after a friendly wrangle with Wooten, who insisted on offering me his bunk, that I retired to rest on the wardroom settee in borrowed blankets and night attire. At 6.30, after a perilous trip in the whaler, Dick and I eventually arrived on board our own ship.

Lucky *Mariner!* Leave at Christmas!

II.

Punctually at seven o'clock the *Mariner* slipped from her buoy and proceeded to sea. The weather had not improved, and once past the line of dancing buoys and the bobbing, drunken-looking red lightship at the harbour-mouth, she found the full force of the gale.

The little ship, speeding along at twenty knots into the teeth of the wind and the angry, curling sea, behaved much as usual—sometimes banged to and fro like a shuttlecock, sometimes wallowing in the welter like a half-tide rock. Clouds of spray went flying high over her bridge and her funnel, to drench everybody on deck; and occasionally, when her

sharp bows fell with a thump into the heart of
an oncoming wave, heavy masses of broken
water came surging along the forecastle to
expend their fruitless energy against the
bridge and the charthouse with a series of
shocks which caused the whole ship to quiver
and tremble. Then the bows would lift
dizzily, and the white-caps, breaking on board
farther aft, went racing madly along the low
deck until the men had literally to hang on by

their eyelids to prevent themselves from being
washed overboard. The motion was abominable, for the *Mariner* leapt and pranced,
pitched and rolled and wallowed, shook and
quivered, all at the same time.

But who cared? Who minded being
wetted to the skin and rattled about like a
pea in a bandbox when 'a little drop o' leaf'
was looming up in the offing? They were off
to refit at a dockyard; and the refit, judging

from the number of defects which had to be made good, would take at least a fortnight. Fourteen whole days! That meant seven days' leave for every officer and man aboard.

Most of them had not set eyes on their wives, families, parents, relations, best girls, or whomever else they took interest in, for months. Some of the men had hardly set foot ashore since the last time the ship refitted, and had been industriously saving up their monthly wages against the time when, the accumulated 'Bradburys' crackling merrily in their pockets, they would be able to make a glorious and most satisfactory splash with their hard-earned money, and d—— all expense.

Every soul on the ship had his own ideas on the subject of leave. Peter Wooten, the lieutenant-commander, would meet his wife in London, and spend three or four days at an hotel. They would do several theatres, and spend much money on taxi-cabs; while Mrs Peter would most certainly intimate her desire to do some shopping, as she hadn't 'a rag fit to be seen in.' She always seemed to run out of respectable garments when Peter went on leave, for she knew well enough that her husband, delighted at seeing her again, would forget all about her overdrawn dress allowance and provide the wherewithal. But, as a *quid pro quo*, she usually insisted on buying him some thick woollen undervests to keep him warm at sea; but the ungrateful recipient, who hated above all things spending money on undergarments and travelling, generally put off the replenishment of his own depleted wardrobe until the last possible moment. When the shopping had all been done, they would spend the rest of the time in visiting other people's houses, where Peter, without being indiscreet or giving away State secrets, would do his best to answer innumerable questions as to what the navy were really doing, and how many U-boats had been sunk during the previous month.

The sub., irrepressible and impecunious, had arranged to have a gay time in the Metropolis with the surgeon-probationer for just as long as their joint finances permitted it. The doc. was eminently capable of acting as the sub.'s bear-leader, for before the war and his appearance in naval uniform he had been a student at a London hospital, where, at some remote period, when hostilities ceased, he would have to return to pass his final examinations before being launched forth as a fully qualified medico. But what he did not know about London was hardly worth talking about. He knew of a cabman's shelter where, at two o'clock in the morning, and for the modest sum of ten-pence, one might, before the days of rationing, procure a huge plate of fried eggs and bacon. By reason of a friendship with a member of the Metropolitan police, moreover, he was by way of being an honorary member of a police canteen where they sold excellent beer in jugs, and sausages and mashed potatoes. There were quite a lot of things he had learnt as a medical student.

But he did not intend personally to conduct the sub. to cabmen's shelters and policemen's canteens. Oh dear, no!

They would take rooms at the same hotel, and rising at ten o'clock in the morning, would live a life of ease and luxury. They would see every revue and musical comedy in London, and then, having lived for three glorious days at the rate of three thousand pounds a year, would shake the dust of the city off their feet, and spend the rest of their leave in the bosoms of their respective families.

The men, of course, would scatter to the four winds of heaven, some to their beloved 'Pompey,' where, since the *Mariner* had a Portsmouth crew, a good many of them had their homes. Others would gravitate to London, or to their parents or their families in the depths of rural England; while the half-dozen Royal Naval Reserve men—MacLeods, MacIvers, and other Macs—would request and obtain forty-eight hours' leave extension to enable them to visit their homes in their own native Scotland.

Leading Seaman Joshua Billings and 'Pincher' Martin, A.B., had a joint establishment at Weymouth. I say they had it, but it was not actually theirs. It really belonged to a Mrs Billings, and consisted of quite a prosperous little newspaper, tobacco, and sweet shop. Before her marriage to Joshua, Mrs Billings had been Mrs Figgins, the relict of a cab-driver; and as Joshua himself was on the verge of retiring from the navy when he married her just before the war, he would not hear of the business being given up. Indeed, though undoubtedly fond of his wife, he had also an idea for the main chance. He had long been on the look-out for some fairly easy method of supplementing his small pension, and the substantial charms of the lady with a satisfactory little business of her own were too good to be missed. To tell the truth, he rather looked forward to the day when, as a gentleman at large in a billy-cock hat and a 'civvy' suit, he should lend the light of his countenance to the establishment, and himself pass the time of day with the more influential customers whilst serving them with their packets of cigarettes and newspapers. 'It's allus a good thing for a pore widdy-woman to 'ave a man about the house,' he had pointed out when pressing his suit for the heart and hand of his adored one; and Mrs Figgins, being evidently of the same opinion herself, blushed rosily and consented to become Mrs Billings.

Mrs 'Pincher' Martin, originally Emmeline Figgins, was Mrs Billings's daughter. She was a pretty, capable-looking young woman of twenty-one, with attractive blue eyes, a fascinating *retroussé* nose, a mass of golden hair, and a habit of saying exactly what she thought. At the outset, during the 'walking out' or courting stage, the course of Pincher's one and only real love affair had not run exactly smooth, but after getting to know each other the two young things had become very devoted

—so devoted that they were married within a
month of Martin's release from the Royal
Naval Hospital at Haslar, where he had been
recovering from a wound received in the battle
of Jutland.

Pincher and his wife had no separate establishment of their own. As Joshua was necessarily at sea until the termination of the war,
mother and daughter lived together. But
Martin had been given to understand that
he could come and go as he pleased. The
arrangement suited him admirably, for, though
he contributed a certain weekly sum towards
household expenses, it was far cheaper for him
than if Emmeline had a house or lodgings
of her own. Moreover, everybody concerned
preferred it.

The little *ménage à deux*, which became a
ménage à quatre whenever Joshua and Pincher
obtained leave at the same time, was a happy
one. The men themselves were never there
long enough for there to be any signs of
discord or friction in the domestic arrangements, so Weymouth was the one place in
the United Kingdom which was ever in their
thoughts.

The trip was a bad one, and bitterly cold;
and the short winter day was again drawing
in when the *Mariner*, her funnels caked white
with dried salt, her decks covered with a layer
of ice from the frozen spray, and icicles
pendent from her mast, rigging, and guns,
steamed up the river on the last few miles
of her journey. She arrived in the midst

of a heavy snow-squall, in which it was impossible to see more than two hundred yards; but, feeling his way cautiously from buoy to buoy, Wooten took her up the tortuous estuary, and made her fast to a mooring-buoy off the dockyard.

At eight o'clock the next morning the lock-gates opened to receive her, and steaming into the basin, escorted by a couple of snorting, fussy-looking dockyard tugs, vomiting forth clouds of noisome black smoke, the destroyer was berthed alongside a wall. Steam was allowed to die down, and at once the ship was invaded by various harassed-looking officials and overseers armed with indelible pencils and defect lists, and hordes of dockyard 'maties' with their donkeys or tool-chests. They arrived not singly, but in their dozens. Workmen of every imaginable trade—shipwrights, horny-handed sons of toil from the engineering and constructive departments, carpenters, plumbers, caulkers, riveters, blacksmiths, painters, riggers, and many more. But they were an orderly mob, for they all knew what to do and where to do it, and presently the ship resounded to the thudding and clanging of hammers as they explored her inner recesses and removed various pieces of machinery in whose welfare they were interested. They were working against time, and ere long the upper deck, already covered in black mud, became littered with a heterogeneous mass of pipes and parts of machinery filched from the bowels of the ship, which would soon be carried off in hand-carts, to be refitted and renovated in the dockyard workshops. The ship seemed to be in a state of rapid disintegration, and Wooten, coming back on deck and seeing the litter of untidiness, heaved a sigh of deep disgust.

But a vessel always looks forlorn and forsaken in a dockyard. In her natural element, the sea, she is a thing of life, a beautiful thing of flesh and blood with a very decided will of her own, whose every whim or idiosyncrasy must be humoured or combated. In a dockyard, however, lying alongside a wall, she seems to lose her entity. Her individuality vanishes, and she becomes for the time being an inert and helpless hull, a faded and bedraggled beauty of chastened appearance, doing her best to appear respectable.

Wooten tramped off through the snow and slush to report his ship's arrival to the commander-in-chief of the port and the admiral superintendent. They were both affability itself, and the kind-hearted C.-in-C. was very indulgent over the matter of leave.

'Send your proposals in to me,' he said, 'but remember that I like both officers and men to get away for as long as they possibly can. It must be pretty cold at sea nowadays, eh?' he added, standing with his back to a roaring fire and gazing at the snow beating against the windows.

'It is, sir,' Wooten agreed.

The admiral nodded and smiled. 'Right,'

he said. 'Send your people away as soon as you can spare them. Good-morning.'

He understood what leave meant; he had been a junior officer himself not so many years ago.

III.

And so it came to pass that, late on Christmas Eve, Joshua Billings and Pincher Martin, each clad in his most immaculate raiment, and each carrying a small bundle done up in a blue-striped hand-kerchief, arrived at the London and South - Western Railway Company's terminus at Water-loo. They arrived in some style —in a taxi-cab, with their feet upon the seats opposite; and, if the truth be known, they had rather dallied by the way, for, with the greater number of the other liberty men from the *Mariner*, they had arrived in London at 5.57. It was now 10.43.

But still, as Joshua had pointed out, Christmas comes but once a year, and a week's leave barely more often; so the Mariners, before separating to King's Cross, Liverpool Street, Euston, Victoria, Paddington, and other London termini, *en route* for their homes, had forgathered at various places of refreshment to celebrate the festive season and their temporary independence. So at 10.43, when Billings and Pincher arrived at Waterloo,

they were both feeling happy with themselves
and the world in general.

After overpaying the taxi-cabman in a
manner which excited that worthy's profound
admiration, they marched solemnly on to the
platform to inquire about the trains for Weymouth. The next one left at 11.55, they were
informed by an inspector, who rather objected
to being clapped on the back and addressed as
'old cock' and 'Mister Funnyface,' so they
had over an hour to wait.

'Look 'ere, now,' Joshua remonstrated with
the official; 'me an' Pincher don't want to
wait an hour, see? 'Aven't you got a hengine
ready wi' steam up for full speed as 'll give us
a passage? It'll be 'arf-a-dollar for you if you
kin fix it up.'

'Don't waste my time,' snapped the inspector, peevish and irritable after a long day's
work and the extra Christmas traffic. 'Who
are you trying to bribe? You know very
well you can't have an engine.'

'Orl right, ole son,' retorted the irrepressible Billings. 'Don't go gettin' dizzy just
becos' I asks a civil question. I'm an infloo-
ential share'older in your company, an' if you
don't be'ave I'll report you, an' 'ave you disrated to porter. See if I don't!'

'I don't care who you are!' rejoined the
harassed official.

'Oh, chuck it!' Pincher broke in, anxious
to avert a quarrel. ''Ere, 'ave a bit o' ship's
'bacca, an' let's make friends.' He fumbled
in his bundle, and produced a couple of inches

of black navy plug, which he thrust into the man's hand.

'Don't mind if I do,' said the inspector, rather more affably, placing the gift in his tail-pocket. 'Thanks, very much.'

'Look 'ere, young fella,' said Billings, seized by a sudden and brilliant inspiration. 'I wants to buy a turkey for th' missus.'

'Turkey!' smiled the railway-man. 'You'll get no turkeys at this time of night.'

Joshua seemed somewhat disconsolate. 'Isn't there no shops near 'ere where they sells 'em?' he inquired.

'There's Cox's, the poulterer's, in Charlotte Street, not more than a couple of hundred yards from the entrance to the station. But he'll be shut by now.'

'We'll ruddy soon make 'im open,' Billings replied. ''Ow do we get there, ole son?'

The directions were duly given, the inspector was wished good-night and a happy Christmas, and ten minutes later two respectable members of His Majesty's naval forces might have been seen holding an anxious colloquy in the dark street outside the shuttered establishment of Mr Ebenezer Cox, fish and poultry merchant.

They spent several minutes hammering at the side-door without avail, and then, raising their voices, shouted in unison.

'Strike me!' exclaimed Pincher, breathing heavily. 'There don't seem to be nobody in the 'ouse, or else they're all dead, or drunk, or somethin'. What'll we do, Josh?'

''Eave bricks at their ruddy windows an'

wake 'em up,' Joshua replied promptly, groping
in the gutter for the necessary missiles. 'It's
downright disgraceful th' time some o' these
'ere shore-goin' folk turns in!'

But not a vestige of a stone or a pebble
could be found, nothing but an ancient banana-
skin and a rusty sardine-tin.

'We'll 'ave to give it up, Pincher boy,'
said Joshua at last. 'I can't find nothin' to
'eave.'

Martin thought for a moment. 'Look 'ere,
Josh. Can you sing?'

'Sing! Me! Wot d'you take me for—a
ruddy canary-bird, or wot?'

''Ardly, chum. But we might pretend we
was carol-singers.'

Billings burst out into a raucous laugh, but
he saw the force of the suggestion. 'It ain't
much in my line,' he said, wiping his lips.
'My singin' ain't wot it used to be. What'll
we sing?'

'"Good King Wenceslas,"' said Pincher,
who thought he could rely on his memory for
the words of the first verse.

'Good king 'oo?' asked Joshua, in some
perplexity.

'Wenceslas. If you don't know the words,
just follow me an' 'um th' toon.'

'Orl right. Start 'er up.'

Pincher cleared his throat and began,
Billings chiming in with a series of throaty
bass rumbles which bore a distinct resemblance
to the blasts of a cracked trombone or the fog-
siren of a lightship.

'Good King Wenceslas looked out
    On th' feast of Stephen,
When the snow lay round about,
    Deep, and crisp, and even.
Brightly shone the moon that night,
    But the frost was cru-u-u-el,
When a pore man '——

The carol was rudely interrupted by the sudden opening of a top window and the emergence of an elderly female head.

'Go away!' it shrilled. 'We don't want none o' your kind 'ere. Why can't you let respectable folk alone, instead o' 'ammerin' at their doors and 'owlin' outside their 'ouses at this time o' night?'

'Orl right, missus,' returned the unperturbed Billings. 'We didn't mean no 'arm. We was merely attractin' your attention. We wants to buy a turkey.'

'Turkey! I haven't got no turkeys. Besides, the shop's been shut this hour or more, and my husband's in bed with the toothache.'

'Look 'ere, ole darlin',' Pincher put in; 'we're two pore, starvin' sailors wot's been defendin' our country. We've just been given a week's leaf, an' we wants a nice li'l' turkey to take 'ome for Christmas. We've got our meat tickets.'

'You can't 'ave one,' said the voice, but rather more agreeably. 'We've nothing but geese left, and them's three-and-two a pound.'

'Don't care if they're three-and-six,' said the opulent Joshua. 'Come on, ole gal, put on your dressin'-gown an' let's 'ave one.'

The head withdrew, and they heard the sounds of conversation within the room.

'All right,' said the lady, popping her head out of the window again like a jack-in-the-box. 'My 'usband says you can 'ave a goose. I 'll be down in a minute.'

'Now then, what's all the row about?' came another voice from the street, as the gleam from a bull's-eye lamp fell on the two bluejackets.

'We 're buyin' a goose, sergeant dear,' said Billings, recognising the helmeted figure of a policeman. 'Me an' my chum, Pincher'——

'You can't come making disturbances at this time o' night,' the constable interrupted gruffly. 'I heard a row like somebody being strangled, and came along to see what was up. Go home quiet, can't you?'

'Our train don't leave till 11.55,' Pincher observed.

The policeman grunted. 'You 're sailors, aren't you?' he asked, flashing his lamp on their cap-ribbons.

'We 're matloes, if that's wot you mean, ole son,' Joshua agreed.

'Know an A.B. of the name o' Horrigan?' asked the policeman.

''Orrigan?' said Pincher, racking his brains. 'Is 'e a fat feller with a ginger beard?'

'No. Long chap, clean shaven, with black hair. He 's serving along o' Admiral Beatty in his flagship.'

'Sorry. I 'aven't met 'im.'

'He 's my brother,' the constable said.

'When he comes on leave he gives me a bit o' tobacco now and then. Good stuff, navy tobacco.'

Billings promptly turned his back and studied the landscape. Pincher laughed.

'Come on, Josh. It's your turn.'

Joshua pretended not to understand.

'My turn?' he asked, turning round. 'Wot d' you mean?'

'Th' orficer wants a bit o' 'bacca out o' your bundle. I whacked it out to the last bloke, you'll remember.'

The leading seaman, seeing no way out of the difficulty, brought out half a pound of navy plug done up in a long prick, cut off a small portion, and handed it across.

'Thanks,' said the policeman. 'Did you say you were buying a goose?'

Billings nodded.

'Want any assistance?'

'No, thanks, sergeant. The ole lady's comin' down in a minit.'

'Right. I'll be getting along, then. Look out you don't make any more noise or you'll get me into trouble. Good-night!'

'Lor' lumme!' Pincher murmured, as the representative of law and order marched off down the street with heavy tread. 'These 'ere London cops ain't 'arf sharks!'

They heard the sound of footsteps, and a moment later the side-door opened to disclose Mrs Cox in an antique dressing-gown and her gray hair done up in curl-papers.

''Ere you are,' she exclaimed, thrusting a

large parcel into Joshua's arms. 'Ere's the best goose we've got. Eight pounds at three-and-four; that'll be twenty-six and eightpence. Where's your meat ticket?'

''Ere,' said Joshua, fumbling in his cap. 'But, 'arf-a-mo', ma. Didn't you say three-and-two a pound? And 'ow do we know wot 'is weight is? We 'aven't seen 'im on the scales.'

'No; and you won't see 'im on the scales,' retorted the lady with some acerbity. 'You can't expec' me to get weighin' things at this time o' night!'

'An' wot about the money? You said three-and-two a pound.'

'Did I?' she snapped. 'Well, I made a mistake. I should have said three-and-four. 'Ow much longer d'you mean to keep me 'ere? Where's your tickets?'

Joshua handed them across. 'Got yer money ready, Pincher?' he asked.

'Money! Wot money?'

'For this 'ere goose, fat-'ead!'

'It was you 'oo ordered it!' Pincher retorted with some warmth.

'Me!' in a voice of the deepest surprise.

'And I'll be catchin' me death o' cold if I stand 'ere much longer,' put in the scantily attired lady. 'Pay me wot you owe me and clear out.'

Billings, murmuring fiercely to himself, fumbled in his trousers-pocket. ''Ere you are, missus,' he said, reluctantly extracting a pound and a ten-shilling note. 'I wants three and fourpence change.'

"'Aven't got no change,' said Mrs Cox, taking the money with alacrity.

'Well, give us somethin' instead,' replied the magnanimous Billings. 'And when you're done with it, I wants me meat ticket back.'

The woman retreated, and presently re-appeared with a moist, odoriferous parcel done up in newspaper. "'Ere you are, young man,' she said, pushing it at Pincher. 'There's some nice dried 'addicks for your breakfuss.— Here's your meat card, Mister Fatty. Good-night!'

'Mister 'ow much?' Billings demanded.

'Fatty,' snapped Mrs Cox, slamming the door in their faces, presently to retire chuckling to bed, well satisfied with the night's business.

Joshua and his friend, clasping their pur-chases, made their way back to the station.

'Strewth!' Pincher murmured, sniffing his parcel dubiously. 'These 'ere fish smells somethin' 'orrid! I believe we've been done, Josh.'

'I expect we 'ave, mate,' his friend agreed mournfully. 'Wot wi' being robbed right and left, and insulted, an' most of me meat coupons pinched, I can see London's no place for the likes of us!'

IV.

The train was exasperatingly slow, and it was not until nearly dawn on Christmas morning that Joshua and Pincher, halting outside the newspaper - shop at Weymouth, deposited their belongings on the doorstep, and proceeded to bombard the establishment with gravel and small stones.

The reply was immediately forthcoming, for a window shot up and a head with two long plaits of hair pendent from it looked out. 'Who's there?'

'Don't you know your own 'usband?' Pincher howled, recognising his wife. ''Ere's Joshua, too. We've got a week's leaf!'

'Why didn't you tell us you were coming?' Emmeline asked excitedly. 'Lawks! Won't mother be pleased?'

'Thought we'd give you both a surprise, me dear,' Joshua laughed. 'Come on, me gal. Shake a leg. Roust out yer ma, an' let us in.'

She needed little encouragement, for the head withdrew, there came the sound of scuttering footsteps and conversation from inside, and presently the door opened and Joshua and Pincher fell into the arms of their respective wives.

'Oh Bill!' Emmeline sighed happily, dragging her man into the little parlour at the back of the shop, and putting her arms round his neck. 'I *am* pleased to see you!'

Pincher's mouth was too full of her hair to answer, but his arms were around her soft waist, and he squeezed her until she gasped for breath, and told him to 'give over.'

Joshua and his better-half were doing the same in the shop itself.

But the goose, a venerable bird which had evidently passed its long life in walking from

John o' Groats to Land's End, was tough,
lean, and very stringy; while the haddocks
were consigned uncooked to the dustbin,
where they were presently discovered by the
cat from next door.

'Oh, you men!' Mrs Billings murmured
reprovingly, her eyes misty with happiness.
'You're nothing but a lot o' babies when it
comes to spending your money. I dunno'
where you'd be if you hadn't got wives to
look after you.'

Joshua laughed, and Pincher, with Emmeline
sitting on his knee, quite agreed.

CHAPTER XI.

THE NIGHT PATROL.

'The maintenance of the Dover Patrol is a story in itself. Occasionally the enemy tries to raid it.'—SIR ERIC GEDDES, 11th July 1918.

I.

THE night was intensely dark, with every indication of rain in the low, heavy-looking clouds and the damp, chilly feeling in the air. The young moon had long since set, but no stars twinkled overhead, for from horizon to horizon the arch of the heavens was shrouded in an impenetrable canopy of velvety, smoky black, with here and there the inkier blackness of bunches and wisps of scattered nimbus trailing lazily to the north-eastward on the wings of some freakish upper air-current.

On the surface it was quite calm, what little breeze there had been during the day having died away at sundown. And now, soon after midnight, the oiliness of the sea was only ruffled in little patches by occasional errant cat's-paws, as gentle breaths of air came stealing fitfully seaward from the direction of the coast.

To the east and the south-east, where lay the land, the undersides of the clouds on the horizon flickered and glowed spasmodically with a dull ruby light reflected from the gleam of distant and invisible gun-flashes. In the same direction, white balls of fire from star-shell and flares soared ceaselessly skywards, now in twos and threes, sometimes in sudden batches of a dozen. They curved over and down, shedding areas of bluish-white light, misty, but very brilliant, until, waning gradually, they fell slowly to earth, to be followed by others. And though those flares were fired ashore in the trenches many miles away, their illumination would have permitted those in the destroyer patrol watching off the coast to read moderate-sized print without difficulty. The trenches themselves must have been bathed in a glare as bright as daylight.

From somewhere on land, far away behind those leaping balls of fire, the narrow, misty beam of a searchlight, terminating abruptly where it met the clouds, wandered uneasily across the low sky. Another, nearer at hand on the coast, wakened into being at intervals, and sent its ray sweeping slowly to and fro across the sea, searching for it knew not what, like a great watching eye.

The still air throbbed in the insistent murmur of heavy gun-fire, now loud like thunder as the offshore breeze freshened, now hushed to a sound like the far-away rolling of many drums, or the soft rumble of a distant goods-train passing through a culvert. It was the song of the Western Front, the ceaseless song which had continued for nearly four years.

To those in the destroyers it was no novelty. No great offensive was in progress. Affairs ashore were in their normal condition, each side holding its own trench-lines, and contenting itself with nightly raids and uninterrupted bombardments of the opposing trenches and back areas. Those whose duty lay afloat had long since become accustomed to the sounds of strife, regarding them, indeed, as being quite in the order of things. Sometimes, when the firing seemed to quicken in its fury, they rather pitied the men fighting in the trenches, wondering vaguely how 'them pore blokes' were getting on, and secretly rather envious at not being able to lend them more of a helping hand in the common cause. But when the wind rose, and the short, curling sea made life a misery and a burden; when, in the bitter winter gales, the driving spray froze as it fell and glued men's mufflers to their necks, covered the always slippery decks with sheet-ice until it was barely possible to stand upright when the ship rolled, and choked the muzzles of the guns with blocks of solid ice, which had to be thawed out with hot water—then it was that the men at sea were jealous of those who fought on land, and had nothing whatsoever to do with that most unstable and unsympathetic element, the sea.

The work of the patrolling destroyers was certainly no sinecure. They had occasional spells off, but sometimes for a fortnight or more they were at it night after night in all weathers, taking what rest they could in the day-time. There had been many 'scraps' with

German torpedo-craft—short, sharp, desperate encounters in the blackness of the night, when the combatants, rushing practically alongside each other at high speed, pumped shell at their opposite numbers at point-blank range, and dodged and twisted madly in their efforts to ram and to use their torpedoes. They were always breathless, rather nerve-racking experiences, these battles in the darkness. They began so suddenly, and when one least expected them. Events succeeded each other with nightmare rapidity, while the element of chance entered hugely into them. One might make up one's mind what to do in fifty different combinations of circumstances, but it was always the fifty-first that happened. The Germans, moreover, though it is true they generally sought safety in flight when once engaged, were desperate fighters when it came to the point, and frequently gave as many hard knocks as they got.

The enemy always had the advantage in that they could emerge from their ports at their own chosen time. There was no knowing when or where they might appear, and the watchers, spread out in groups over a large area, had always to be ready. When, as it sometimes happened, month after month passed without incident, the work of the patrols, always arduous, seemed rather purposeless and monotonous. The inactivity—to call it that for want of a better word, for they were always busy—might have lulled some people into a sense of false security, encouraged them to relax their efforts, to take things a little more easily.

But not so these men. There was hardly a destroyer working in the area which, at one time or another, had not been blooded in actual close-quarter conflict with the Boche. Every officer and man knew his work. Each one of them realised that the ship which sighted the enemy before the enemy sighted her, and was thus enabled to get in the first salvo of shell, or the first torpedo, generally had the opponent at her mercy. Even if the foe appeared in superior strength it mattered little. Again and again it had been proved by actual experience that these night destroyer actions normally ended in close-range *mêlées*, in which, before very long, the ships of both sides became hopelessly mixed. So superiority in numbers was usually countered by surprise. In other words, the side which struck first, and struck hard, generally won.

Moreover, and what was far more important, these outlying destroyers were the advanced sentries for a complicated system of other patrols behind them, not to mention an army of other craft—auxiliary patrol-vessels engaged in their usual task of hunting and harrying submarines, transports and hospital-ships passing to and fro across the Channel, merchantmen—ships of every possible persuasion and calling.

There had been regrettable incidents in the past, when German destroyers, favoured by mist and low visibility, had slipped through the cordon of watchers to bombard towns, to sink and destroy ships, and had succeeded in making their escape without being brought to action. Such things did not happen through any defect in organisation, or through any lack of zeal or energy on the part of the patrols. They were merely the outcome of bad luck, the ever-changing fortune of war.

Nevertheless, when such incidents took place, certain sections of the public press raised their voices and clamoured mercilessly for somebody's blood, inquiring, in terms both impolite and acid, what the navy was thinking about to permit such goings-on.

They little knew the conditions in which the patrols worked, did not realise a tithe of their responsibility, or that, to any seaman, it was manifestly impossible for every square mile of sea in the Strait to be watched and guarded constantly. They forgot that the hostile raids, regrettable though they might be, were only part and parcel of the ebb and flow of war. It is impossible to make omelets without breaking eggs, impossible to make war without loss; while, after all, the sallies which the Germans occasionally indulged in with varying success were only comparable to those nightly raids in the trenches.

No; some people ashore who had the satisfaction of sleeping in their beds every night of their lives forgot that there had been no appreciable tightening of their belts, and quite omitted to remember to what and to whom this was due.

And the navy, when attacked by the Scribes and the Pharisees, its own country-men, those whom it fed and defended, merely shrugged its shoulders and said nothing. It had been pilloried in the past, and would doubtless be pilloried in the future. It knew the fickleness of public opinion; recollected, with some little bitterness, that at one port men wounded at the battle of Jutland had been hissed and execrated while being carried ashore on their blood-stained stretchers.

Such things should not be, but unhappily are; so the Sea Service, being wise in its generation and too proud to explain, smiled, said nothing, and—continued to do its duty without the plaudits of the multitude.

The watchers continued to watch.

II.

On board the *Minx*, the third destroyer in the line, M'Call, the first lieutenant, was keeping the first two hours of the middle watch. He stood close to the bridge-screens, using his glasses continually to sweep the horizon, with an ever-watchful eye upon the black smudge and the dim trail of phosphor-escent water which showed the position of the ship next ahead, a cable distant. Occasionally, as the ship crept up or dropped astern of her station, or sheered a little out of the line, he flung an order over his shoulder to the man at the revolution telegraph, or to the helmsman

The helmsman twiddling his wheel as he peered into
the dimly lit compass-bowl.

PAGE 254.

twiddling his wheel as he peered into the dimly lit compass-bowl, the men repeating the orders word for word, to show they had been heard and understood.

Besides M'Call himself, the quartermaster, and the man at the engine-room telegraphs, space had also to be found on the small bridge for a couple of A.B.'s, who had nothing to do but keep a constant look-out to port and to starboard, a leading signalman, the messenger, and two more men, whose duty was to attend to the instruments and the voice-pipes communicating with the guns and the torpedo-tubes. There was hardly room to move, no space whatsoever to walk up and down.

At the first lieutenant's feet, coiled up in an impossible attitude in a deck-chair tucked in under the chart-table, lay Langlands, the lieutenant-commander, seemingly asleep. He and his second in command invariably spent the entire night on the bridge when the ship was on patrol, relieving each other every couple of hours for the doubtful comfort of the deck-chair. It was a miserable sleeping-billet at the best of times, and bitterly cold; while as often as not one or both of the officers spent the hours of darkness without a wink of actual sleep. But neither would dare trust himself off the bridge for a moment when there was the least possibility of the enemy being sighted. It was their station in action.

The sub., lucky fellow, spent his watch below, slumbering more or less peacefully on the settee in the charthouse, a concession he generally made up for by keeping extra watch in the day-time. As for the gunner and the midshipman, R.N.V.R., the latter a young gentleman who was still at a public school in 1916, they, fully dressed, were sleeping, or pretending to sleep, in some hole or corner near the stations they would occupy in action, the 'snotty' somewhere in the forepart of the ship, near the foremost four-inch gun, and the gunner by his beloved torpedo-tubes. The engineer - lieutenant and the surgeon - probationer were the only officers who could turn in in their clothes with really clear consciences, though the former had elected to make himself a bivouac on deck with blankets, a rug, and an air-pillow within six feet of the hatch leading to his engine-room. He was a wise man, was the engineer officer, and a married man with a large family. He had once been in the wardroom of a destroyer when a mine exploded under the stern, and since that distressing experience he preferred being on deck. The surgeon - probationer either did not know of, or did not care for, such things. He lay stretched out on a settee in the stuffy wardroom, snoring blissfully.

Men, some dozing, but the majority wide awake, lay clustered round the guns, the torpedo-tubes, or the searchlight, prepared for an instant summons. Shell and cartridges were piled in all the gun-positions, where the loading numbers could find them easily in the dark; while at various places on deck were bundles of cutlasses, and rifles with magazines charged and scabbarded bayonets fixed, ready for immediate use in the event of running alongside an enemy and boarding. All the officers and some of the men carried automatic pistols or revolvers in belts strapped round their thick lammy coats ; while two unshaven gentlemen, one an ex-grocer's assistant from Bermondsey, and the other a Glasgow news-paper-boy, presided drowsily over a couple of machine-guns.

In a word, the ship was prepared for action. A single touch on the bell-push on the bridge by the first lieutenant's elbow would set the alarm-gongs jangling and bring the men jump-ing to their feet.

The night, except for that constant rumble of gun-fire in the east, was very still. There was no whistling of wind through the rigging, nothing but the hiss, gurgle, and liquid splutter of the bow-wave as the ship moved through the water, the deep humming of the stokehold fans, and the occasional shrill, protesting cry of a startled and indignant diver disturbed in his beauty-sleep on the water and scuttering clumsily for safety.

The sub., in the charthouse, awakened by the conversation of the gun's crew sitting on deck outside, was softly anathematising them.

' I met 'er at the cinema last time I was on long leaf,' said a voice. ' Fine, strappin' gal she was. Reg'lar little bit of all right. She takes a fancy to me the minute '——

' Go hon, you ruddy old Bluebeard !' came

a gruff interjection. 'What about that other gurl I used to see you walkin' out with?'

'Can't 'elp the other gal,' was the rather indignant reply. 'She played me false. I found out she was bein' courted by a lance-corpril belongin' to a bantam reg'ment. I 'ad a dust-up with 'im about it; but she weren't worth fightin' over, so I just said 'e could bloomin' well 'ave 'er. This one I'm tellin' you about takes a fancy to me the moment she claps eyes on me.'

'She can't know much about you, Shiner.'

'What d'you mean? Can't know much about me!' with some acerbity. 'What d'you mean, speakin' like that? Why should she want to know about me? She loves me at first sight, I tells you!'

'Go hon, you old liar!' was the polite retort.

'S'welp me, she did! She takes me 'ome to see 'er pa and ma, and they likes me, too, 'cos they asks me to stay and 'ave a bit o' supper. 'Er pa works in Pompey dockyard. 'E and 'is missus likes their drop o' gargle now and then, so the nex' night I does the polite and treats 'em all to seats at the 'Ippodrome, and a bit o' somethin' t'eat at a restorong afterwards. Cost me more'n 'arf-a-quid, that did. And now it's all fixed up proper, and me and Lucy gets married nex' time I goes on long leaf. Fine, strappin' bit o' fluff, she is. Got a bit o' money in the bank, too!'

'Can't you fellers let a bloke get a drop o' sleep, 'stead o' chawin' your fat all the bloomin'

night?' growled a new and very irritated voice.
''Oo wants to hear about your love conquests,
Shiner?'

'I'll 'ave you know I'm engaged to the
young lady,' came the dignified answer. 'Any
bloke what says a word agin' 'er gets a punch
on the nose! See?'

'Well, you might let other blokes get a bit
o' sleep, anyhow.'

'Oh, go to 'ell!' said Shiner wrathfully.
'You don't know what bein' in love feels like.
'Oo's goin' to fall in love with a bloke with a
face like yourn?'

'Ssh!' hissed some one. 'Don't get having
a barging-match, you two. You'll wake Little
Jimmy in a minute. He's asleep in the charthouse.'

'Oh, go to 'ell!' retorted the amorous one.

The sub-lieutenant, rather pleased that his
newly discovered lower-deck nickname was
not 'Dirty Dick' or 'Sweaty Sam,' chuckled
softly to himself, examined his wrist-watch,
discovered he had still over an hour before he
was due on the bridge, and rolled over and
went to sleep again.

III.

Presently, as the destroyers reached the
limit of their patrol, M'Call, on the bridge,
saw the long, dark shadow of the leader
swinging out of the line as she altered
course to starboard to proceed in the opposite direction.

'Captain, sir,' he said, bending down to

shake the recumbent figure in the deck-chair by the shoulder, 'they're altering course.'

'Right!' grunted the lieutenant-commander, sitting up and fumbling for his pipe. 'Follow 'em round. Are we up to time?'

'To the minute, sir. The tide's been against us during the last run.'

'Right! Let's see. High-water's at 1.42, our time, isn't it?'

'Yes, sir.'

'So, if we have to go skiboosting about over these blessed banks after the Huns, there'll be water enough for us up till about half three—what?'

'There or thereabouts, sir. We might say four o'clock at a pinch.'

'That be blowed for a yarn!' smiled the C.O. 'Not in these trousers! What about that fellow who smashed up his rudder and propellers the other day by leaving it a bit too late? The Court of Inquiry had his blood, all right; and I'll be shot if you'll persuade me to become a burnt-offering!'

'You mean the *Galeka*, sir?' laughed the first lieutenant, watching the next ahead as her helm went over. 'Of course! It's become a habit with her. Sheds propellers by the dozen, and is always in dock expectin' other people to do her dirty work. Damn stoopid, I call it. What sort of a ship goes messin' about on an eight-foot bank, and she drawin' ten and a bit? *We* don't do silly things like that, thank the Lord! Not often, anyhow.—Port fifteen, quartermaster!'

The lieutenant-commander seemed rather amused.

'The *Galeka* made a mistake of an hour over this beastly B.S.T. business,' he pointed out. 'I don't wonder at it, personally; but if I were you, Number One, I shouldn't say too much. She's not the only one who's slipped up, not by a very long chalk. What about the time you'——

'Port twenty!' M'Call interrupted, anxious to avoid a question which he had every reason to know would be awkward. 'Ease to ten!' as the ship swung round after her leader. ''Midships!—Meet her starboard!—Steady!— What was it you were going to say, sir?' he inquired.

'I've forgotten now,' Langlands yawned. 'But let me know when we turn again, and if I find you astern of station you'll be hanged, drawn, and blooming well quartered.'

'I will bear it in mind, sir,' replied Number One, quite unperturbed.

It must have been about twenty minutes later that M'Call, who was intently watching the horizon through his glasses, grunted with surprise. Was his imagination at fault, or had he really seen something—something vaguely white and indistinct—far away in the darkness?

'Starboard look-out,' he asked, lowering his binoculars to wipe the object-glasses, 'did you see anything fine on the starboard bow just now?'

'Thought I saw a sort o' sudden splash,' the

man answered. 'Thought maybe 'twas a fish jumpin', or a breakin' sea, sir.'

'Can't have been a sea,' said M'Call, rather puzzled; 'it's flat calm.'

'That's what it looked like to me, sir,' the seaman protested, rather annoyed at being doubted. 'There, sir!' after a pause; 'there it is again!' He pointed at a glimmer of white with a triumphant forefinger.

The officer's glasses flew to his eyes, and the briefest inspection satisfied him that the man was right, for there slowly crept into his field of vision a ghostly-looking streak of whitened, splashing water. He did not linger an instant, but shouting, 'Action!' pressed the bell-push in front of him.

The time was twelve and a half minutes to two.

The alarm-gongs whirred and jangled throughout the ship, and even as their strident chatter died away he could hear the men bestirring themselves on deck, and the shuffling of feet as they closed up round their guns.

'Action stations!' roared a voice. 'Show a leg, boys! Look lively now!'

'What is it?' asked Langlands, already on his feet.

'Bow-waves on the starboard bow, sir!'

'All right,' the skipper answered, seemingly quite unmoved by the information, but feeling his heart fluttering with excitement. 'I'll take the ship. You look after the gunnery.'

'Ay, ay, sir.—Hicks!'

'Sir?'

'Pass down: All guns load with lyddite; bearing — green,* three, five; range — one, four, double o; deflection—one, five, right.'

'That's them all right!' murmured the captain, with his glasses to his eyes, as the dim flicker of a flaming funnel broke out of the darkness. 'Damn bad stoking, too! Is the sub. up here?'

'Yes, sir.'

'Warn the tubes to be ready to starboard. Don't fire until you get orders.'

'Increasing speed, sir!' sang out a signal-man, as the lumped-up water in the wake of the destroyer ahead grew whiter and more distinct. 'Leader altering course to starboard, sir!'

Langlands, his glasses still levelled on the approaching enemy, flung an order over his shoulder to the man at the telegraph, and the *Minx*, throbbing to the increased thrust of her turbines, darted forward.

The glimmering bow-waves were now clearly visible to the naked eye, and even as the commanding officer watched them, he saw first the whitened trails of water in the wake of several fast-moving vessels, and then the long, blurred smudges of the ships themselves, dimly silhouetted against a lighter patch on

* The side on which a target happens to be is always passed down as 'green' or 'red,' to avoid possible confusion between the words 'starboard' and 'port.' The order 'Green—three, five,' would mean that the guns were to be laid on an object on the starboard side, 35° from right ahead. Similarly, 'Red—one, two, o,' would signify that the target was to port, 120° from right ahead.

the horizon. They were something over a mile distant.

'How many d'you make out, Number One?' he asked.

'Three or four, sir,' said M'Call, putting his lips to a voice-pipe to pass another order to the guns.

'They don't seem to have spotted us,' the captain went on. 'Perhaps they can't see us against the dark background to the west'ard. —Are you all ready?'

'Yes, sir. Quite ready.'

The natural sound of his own voice comforted him, for Langlands, though certainly no coward, was not one of those abnormal men who could saunter through the very gates of hell without trepidation in their hearts. In such people heroism and calmness in the face of danger is a natural habit which can cost them little. They actually do not know what fear is, and hence have no difficulty in combating it.

Another species of bravery altogether is shown by those who feel fear, but can manage to stifle it—can make their will triumph over the perfectly natural desire for personal safety.

And Langlands had this quality. He had been in action many times; but always, before the firing began, his sensations were the same—a ghastly dread of the unexpected, a sickly feeling of apprehension, and an apparent loss of control of his body and limbs, as if his muscles were suddenly made of jelly. But his mind was ever active in such conditions. His brain worked fast and clearly, and outwardly his demeanour was just the same as usual. The fear he felt in his innermost heart never made itself manifest. He had trained himself to conceal it, and even went so far as to smoke a pipe in action to convince others that he was in no way perturbed. Artificiality perhaps, but his men noticed it, and took courage.

It was the suspense that was so intolerable, the awful period of waiting between the time the enemy were sighted and the firing of the first shot. It might be seconds or it might be minutes; but it always seemed hours—hours of mental anguish and nerveracking anxiety. Once under fire, however, these sensations left him altogether, and all thoughts of his own personal safety, all terror of the unknown, were brushed aside. He became cool and alert. Then followed the period of wild exultation when his chief desire was ever the same—to get to close quarters; to fight, if need be, with his bare fists. Realisation, he found, was never quite so bad as anticipation. It was the thinking beforehand of what might happen that was so maddeningly unnerving.

The orders for the destroyers on patrol were very simple and elastic, and all the commanding officers knew exactly what was expected of them. They knew the exact speed at which the leader intended to fight, and that, until they came into close action, they had only to conform to his movements.

Complications really began when the engagement became general and the formation was broken, for then it was a case of each ship for herself, her duty to single out an opponent, and, if possible, to stick to him until he was crippled or sunk.

They were at liberty to use their own initiative, taking what chances they were offered of ramming or of using their torpedoes, and utilising their gun-fire to the best possible advantage. Beyond that, nothing else much mattered; and if, in the *mêlée* which was almost bound to ensue, any friendly vessel had the ill-fortune to be stopped or sunk, it was an understood thing that her crew would have to take their chance until the close of the engagement. Their mates could not break off the action to succour them. The orders were very definite on one point—that while a British ship could steam and a British gun could fire, the raiders were to be pursued, hotly engaged, and reported.

By this time the enemy was at a distance of little more than a thousand yards, and, still steaming fast on a roughly parallel and opposite course, seemed quite oblivious of the presence of the British. It was scarcely possible that he had not sighted them, for even with the naked eye Langlands could clearly see the humped-up, unfamiliar shapes of the German destroyers, with their two squat funnels standing nearly upright, the tall masts aft, and the shorter ones forward. There was no mistaking them.

Perhaps they took the British for friends.
Maybe they were merely reserving their fire,
or were trusting to their speed to slip past
without giving battle, for not a light twinkled
down their line, not a gun roared out. They
still steamed steadily on, grim, menacing, and
silent. There were five of them.

The flotillas must have been drawing
together at a combined speed of fifty knots,
possibly more, and if both continued their
courses they would flash by each other at a
distance of about four hundred yards. And
at fifty knots, one thousand yards is covered
in thirty-six seconds; but still the British
leader held steadily on his course. The
seconds dragged — the enemy came nearer
and nearer—the suspense became maddening.
Langlands felt his heart thumping like a
sledge-hammer. Was the leader missing his

opportunity? It seemed as if in another few seconds it would be too late!

But the senior officer was an old hand at the business, and knew what he was about, and at exactly the right moment his helm went over, and Langlands saw the leading destroyer swerving abruptly to starboard until she was heading straight for the centre of the hostile line. It was evidently the senior officer's intention to attempt to ram the fourth or fifth ship, leaving those ahead to the other destroyers under his orders. It was the plan agreed upon, the plan they all knew by heart.

There came a blaze of greenish-golden flame and the crash of a ragged salvo as the leader's guns opened the ball. A little cluster of spray fountains, white and shimmering, leapt out of the dark sea close to the leading German, and almost before they had tumbled out of sight the guns were flashing all down the hostile line. In another instant every British ship replied and the firing became general.

The time was 1.49.20.

The guns were firing at point-blank range, so that careful aiming, even if it had been possible, was unnecessary. The din became deafening as the loading numbers crammed projectiles and cartridges home, the breeches of the guns slammed to, and the gun-layers pressed their triggers and fired. The air thudded and shook. Intermingled with the deep roaring of the heavier weapons came the unmistakable stutter of the two-pounder pom-poms as they fell to work to sweep the

opposing bridges and decks, and the shriller
stammering of Lewis guns and Maxims. Projectiles screeched and whinnied overhead, burst
with a dull, crashing explosion, and sent their
fragments humming and hissing through the
air to strike funnels, hull, and deck fittings
with an insistent jangling clatter like pebbles
in a tin can. Machine-gun bullets sprayed
past in droves, swishing and crackling as they
came like raindrops through foliage.

Langlands, all but blinded by the brilliant
flashes of the *Minx's* guns, held steadily on
his course. The water round the ship seemed
to be spouting and boiling with falling shell,
and all he could see of the enemy was the
flashes of their guns bursting out redly through
a leaping curtain of shell-geysers, and clouds
of dense, rolling smoke. The Germans seemed
to be altering course a little, for the ship the
Minx was making for, the third in the line,
was drawing slightly across the bows.

' Port ten !' he ordered breathlessly, intent
on running her down.

' Port ten it is, sir,' came the deep voice of
the coxswain, as he twirled the wheel.

' 'Midships ! Steady so, Baker !'

' Steady it is, sir !'

A searchlight from some ship in the German
line flickered into brilliance, illuminated the
scene for an instant in its sickly glare, and
then was suddenly extinguished.

There came a crash, an explosion, and a
momentary blaze of reddish fire from amidships, as a shell drove home by the *Minx's*

after-funnel; but Langlands paid little heed, for the ship still sped on. Another projectile detonated on the water close under the bow, and a signalman on the bridge sat down with a grunt of stupefied astonishment, and began cursing softly to himself. The coxswain, with his right arm broken by a piece of the same shell, groaned audibly as he tried to use the limb and felt the jagged ends of the bone grating horribly together. He suffered excruciating torment, for, unknown to himself, another sliver of red-hot steel had penetrated the muscles of his back. He was in agony, but he still watched the captain, waiting for his next order, and casting an occasional glance at the compass before him to keep the ship on her course.

A red Very light, soaring aloft, bathed the scene in a momentary flush of crimson before, curving over, it fell hissing into the water. The crashing, thudding medley still went on, but above the din M'Call could be heard passing orders like an automaton, and without a tremor in his voice. He passed his orders, but he little knew that the man below whose duty it was to transmit them to the guns was stretched out on deck, slowly sobbing his life away.

'Can I fire, sir?' suddenly screamed the sub., hoarse with excitement.

'Yes!' the captain shouted back, without turning his head.

And a moment later, when the boy saw the flame-spouting silhouette of the enemy's leader in line with the sights of his instrument, he pressed an ebonite knob, shouted through a voice-pipe, and looked anxiously aft. He was rewarded, for he saw the dull, bluish flash and the silvery streak of a torpedo as it leapt from its tube and plunged with a splash into the water. Where that particular torpedo went he never knew, for there was no resultant explosion.

But an instant or two later, when the second German came in line, he pressed another knob. The range at the time seemed absurdly short, and the enemy flashed by in an instant, but the weapon went home. It seemed to strike her fairly amidships, for there came a lurid blast of flame and a cloud of grayish smoke and spray, followed by the roar of an explosion which for a moment completely drowned the sound of the guns.

'Got her, by George!' the sub. muttered softly to himself, watching her as the turmoil subsided and he caught a glimpse of the dripping bow and stern of the enemy's ship lifting themselves out of the water, with the middle portion sagging horribly. 'Clean in halves!'

He had never seen the effect of a torpedo before, and could hardly believe his eyes.

Then several things seemed to happen all at once.

A torpedo fired by the enemy, travelling on the surface in a flutter of spray, suddenly shot past within ten feet of the *Minx's* bows, and almost at the same moment the destroyer astern of the one which had been torpedoed crashed into her helpless consort with a grinding, splintering thud which could almost be felt. The firing from both ships ceased abruptly, and a chorus of shouts and screams came out of the darkness.

The collision occurred within about two hundred feet of the *Minx's* bows, so close and on such a bearing that Langlands could hardly avoid the tangle.

'Hard a-starboard!' he yelled, however, unwilling to risk damaging his own vessel by running down an enemy which must already be helpless through having been collided with by a friend. 'Hard a-starboard, Baker!'

The coxswain flung the wheel over with all his strength, but it was too late.

The ship slewed, but a moment later Langlands caught a hasty glimpse of the black hull of his enemy right under the bows. He found himself looking down on her deck; could see the blurred, white faces of her men as they stared up at him; heard their frightened screams as they saw this new monster bearing down upon them to complete their destruction. It must have been a terrifying sight, the towering, V-shaped bow tearing remorselessly towards them at over twenty knots, with the twin bow-waves leaping and playing on each side of the sharp stem.

A gun roared off from somewhere close at hand, and with the orange flash of it Langlands felt his cap whirled off his head and something strike him across the forehead. A warm gush streamed down his face; but in the excitement of the moment he scarcely noticed it.

The next instant the ship struck.

There was a rending, shuddering thud, the shrill, protesting sound of riven steel, and then a sudden cessation of speed. The hostile destroyer, struck in the stern, twisted round with the force of the blow, and heeled bodily over until the water poured over the farther edge of her deck. Then the *Minx's* bows tore their way aft, splintering, grinding, and crunching—enlarging the enormous wound, wrenching off the side plating, and allowing the water to pour in. The stern of the enemy slid free, and it could be heard slithering along the starboard side as the *Minx* still drove ahead.

The time was exactly 1.52. Four and a half minutes since the enemy had been sighted; two and a half since the first gun had been fired. It had seemed an eternity.

Out of the corner of his eye Langlands caught sight of the shape of one of his friends, spouting flame, driving past to starboard and circling madly across the *Minx's* bows; while another shadow, vague and indistinct in a smoke-cloud, and with guns silent, flashed past, travelling to the north-eastward at high speed. It was the German leader escaping.

For a while the flashes of guns still broke out of the darkness from the direction in which the scattered remnant of the enemy, pursued and hotly engaged, were flying for their lives. The flashes gleamed golden and ruby, while an occasional shell-burst showed up as a flicker of smoky scarlet. The flashes receded farther and farther towards the horizon, and the sobbing, pulsating thunder waned gradually, fainter and fainter, as the combatants steamed away. Then the rolling thud of a distant heavy explosion, and save for the dull mutter of the guns ashore the night was still.

About an hour later, when the pursuers returned, they found nothing but an area of sea strewn with the wreckage of sunken ships, the unmistakable flotsam of battle. They lingered on the spot to rescue several badly wounded and half-drowned Germans who cried piteously for help; but of the *Minx* there was no trace.

'*Minx!* Oh, *Minx!*' they asked by wireless. '*Minx!* where are you?'

But the *Minx* did not answer, and it was with a touch of sadness in their triumphant hearts that the victors picked their way back over the rippling sandbanks towards the anchorage in the golden-gray light of the dawn.

IV.

The rain-clouds had cleared away, but with the advent of daylight a dense sea-fog lay close and thick upon the water; and through it three battle-scarred destroyers steamed wearily but proudly home towards a certain English port whither they had been ordered for necessary repairs.

All three exhibited plain traces of the fight.

One, with an enormous gash on the water-line in the engine-room, caused by a bursting shell which had put the port turbine out of action, limped painfully along at a bare ten knots, with her pumps working to keep down the flow of water, and a collision-mat plastered over the orifice. Another, the leader, had her bridge wrecked, her foremost four-inch gun useless, and a number of jagged holes through the forecastle; while the gray hulls, upper works, and funnels of all three were torn and perforated by shell-splinters, and mottled here and there by the unmistakable yellow splashes and charred paint where projectiles had struck and detonated. They looked as if they had undergone a severe gruelling, as indeed they had; but their casualties were remarkably light—no more than seven killed and thirteen wounded.

It was nearly noon when, with new White Ensigns fluttering gaily from their mizzens, they steamed jauntily into harbour through the entrance between the well-known gray stone breakwaters, each crowned with its white lighthouse.

The fog had cleared a little. The time of their arrival had been reported by wireless, and as they entered a bunch of signal-flags went up to the truck of the admiral's flagstaff ashore. An instant later the men-of-war at their moorings seemed suddenly to swarm with men.

'Oh lor!' grunted the senior officer of the incoming destroyers, realising what was about to happen as he conned his ship from the battered bridge. 'Hell and scissors! I always feel such a damned idiot on these occasions! Never know what to do.'

And a few moments afterwards, as the leader passed within a hundred feet of a huge, blister-sided monitor, the signal ashore came down with a rush, and the monitor's men, waving their caps, broke into a roar of frenzied and uncontrolled cheering, which was taken up by ship after ship. It was no ordinary three cheers. It was a noise like the yelling of the crowd when a goal is scored at a popular football match, a deep-throated bellow which reverberated across the water and echoed and re-echoed from the cliffs. It was an encouraging sound, a sound of good-feeling and good-fellowship, very genuine and spontaneous; and nobody can make more din than the sailorman when he is happy and really puts his heart into it.

The sea-front was densely packed with civilian spectators, who had heard vague rumours of a naval engagement, and even they shouted themselves hoarse and waved parasols, hats, and handkerchiefs as the three destroyers slid up to their buoys.

'I'm glad they're pleased,' murmured the senior officer, blushing a rosy red and rubbing his unshaven chin. 'I do feel a sanguinary fool, though, and I wish to Heaven they'd stop their beastly row! I can't hear myself think.'

'Signal, sir,' said the yeoman of signals, who

had been busy with his telescope. ' " Vice-admiral to division. Well done. Congratulate you most heartily on your success. Admiral would like to see commanding officers when convenient. *Minx* reports " '——

'*Minx!*' shouted the S.O. in delighted astonishment. ' Has she got back, then?'

'Seems so, sir,' said the yeoman, looking round with his telescope. ' Yes, sir,' after a pause. ' That's her! They're just putting her into the floating dock. Her bows are smashed up somethin' crool, and her topmast has gone over the side.'

'Ah, that accounts for our getting no answer to our wireless signals,' murmured the commander. ' Thank Heaven, she's in, though!'

He meant it.

.   .   .   .   .   .

' On the night of the 28th–29th four of our destroyers on patrol met five enemy craft on their way to take part in a raid in the Channel. A hot engagement ensued, in the course of which three of the enemy were sunk. The other two, hit repeatedly and hotly pursued to their base, succeeded in escaping in a badly damaged condition, though from aerial recon-naissance it is believed that one of them sub-sequently foundered. We lost no ships, and our casualties, considering the close range at which the action was fought, were very slight. All the next of kin have been informed.'— *Official Communiqué.*

CHAPTER XII.

THE CONVOY.

I.

THE misty dawn broke over a calm, unruffled sea; but in spite of the promise of fair weather, the senior officer of the escort force, a commander in one of the destroyers, was in no very amiable frame of mind. He had been up most of the night, snatching an odd twenty minutes now and then in a deck-chair on the bridge to rest his weary limbs; but for all his own watchfulness, and the persistent activity of the destroyers under his orders, daylight found the bluff-bowed freighters of his convoy spread over a larger area of sea than was compatible with safety. They were passing through a submarine-infested area, an area in which Fritz had already taken a substantial toll in sinkings.

The destroyers acted the part of watch-dogs and whippers-in, and day and night they were busy, urging on the laggards, checking the runaways, coaxing, persuading, and bully-ing by turns. They encouraged the Nor-wegian who announced plaintively that, owing to the inefficiency of her firemen and the inferiority of her coal, she could steam no more than six and a quarter knots; satisfied the tramp with eight degrees of deviation in her antiquated compass that the course steered was not taking the procession towards the Arctic Circle. The attendant craft zig-zagged here and there like sheep-dogs, dart-ing round from flank to flank to round up those of their unwieldy flock who evinced a desire to dally by the wayside, barking at the tail of the crowd to keep them closed up and compact.

But still the convoy had straggled during the night, so that the commander responsible for their safety was distinctly peevish and irritable. And presently, when it became light enough for signals to be read, he draped his stumpy mast in strings of parti-coloured bunting, while his semaphore wagged lustily, and his destroyers scurried hither and thither on their old, old game of urging on the dawdlers.

With a collection of about twenty mer-chantmen, no two of them capable of exactly the same speed, some hardly able to under-stand the King's English, and most of them seemingly blessed with a spirit of perversity and a sweet desire to do exactly as they liked, when they liked, it was no easy matter to keep them in more or less orderly formation, or to make them realise that straggling from the main body was merely giving any prowl-ing U-boat the tempting opportunity he so fervently desired.

Moreover, the International Code of Signals, excellent though it may be for peace-time purposes, did not lend itself to the rapid manœuvring of an armada, and Morse messages spelt slowly out on a dim flashing lamp from the bridge of a destroyer were apt to be misunderstood, particularly with a disgruntled Scandinavian at the other end. Some of the convoy had proper signalmen, but some had not, and it was a little mortifying when a simple message, 'You are showing a light on the port quarter. Extinguish it at once,' was solemnly interpreted to an astonished and unmarried merchant skipper as, 'You are leaving your wife to the port master. Eztpngulsh him at once!'

The British shipmasters, excellent fellows that they were, got better at the work every day. They no longer shrieked on their whistles and charged madly out of the line when they saw another ship within half a mile of them. They obeyed orders, and regarded the destroyers as their friends, those who would rescue them even at the peril of their own lives if the worst came to the worst and Fritz got home with a torpedo.

But the neutrals—oh heavens, the neutrals! In this particular convoy they outnumbered the British by more than four to one, and were really the cause of all the trouble and the bane of everybody's existence. It was not their war. Until they actually saw a submarine, or got torpedoed, they seemed to regard the whole business with a stolid, bovine apathy, and to consider the escorting destroyers, with their continual signals and remonstrances, as an unmitigated nuisance. When anybody did get torpedoed, as sometimes happened, they suffered from what the commander politely called 'the staggers,' darting erratically this way and that, with no thought for any one's safety but their own. There was no persuading them by any ordinary common-sense methods. They had to be cajoled and driven; so the navy, like the sister-service in Flanders, swore horribly.

It was half-past four in the morning, a time of day when people's livers, if they are at all inclined that way, are more hobnailed than usual, and when no man loves his neighbour as he really should. The commander, moreover, was suffering from lack of regular exercise. Four hours later, at 8.30, breakfast would have been eaten, a sleepless night forgotten, and affairs might have assumed a more cheerful aspect. He might even think of retiring to his charthouse for a shave, a luxury in these days, when—since a submarine might make her attack at any moment—he daren't go down to his cabin for twenty minutes for a hot sponge-down and a change of clothing. He was used to going dirty, however; accustomed to remaining in the same garments from the time the ship left harbour until she returned, though sometimes the trips lasted for as long as five days, occasionally a full week. Then thirty-six or forty-eight hours in harbour, followed by another jaunt out and back.

It was worrying, anxious work, for it never gave one much peace. It was only alleviated by the regular five days' spell for boiler-cleaning each month, and the periodical refits in a dockyard every four or five months, when officers and men snatched what leave they could. But always it seemed as if the human machine were expected to go on running indefinitely, for it was only when the ships themselves gave out that those who manned them got any real rest.

What could one expect? Destroyers were wanted everywhere and for every purpose, and they were now doing work which was unheard of before 1914. Their numbers had increased enormously since the outbreak of war; but even if the output had been twice as large, they would still have been overworked. So it was a time when people were thankful for small mercies—grateful for an extra hour or two in harbour, blessing their luck for fine weather at sea.

The day wore on, and by half-past six the heat of the sun and a freshening breeze had dispelled the mist of early morning. The sea, stirred into minute corrugations, had lost its glassy sheen, and now presented a great velvety expanse of the purest, softest sapphire, darkening here and there to amethyst where cloud-shadows travelled lazily across its surface.

Presently, below the cloud-dappled sky to the north-east, a dim, narrow streak over the hard edge of the horizon gave the first indication of the land; and twenty minutes later the blue, serrated line of the distant coast showed clear and distinct against its background of pale turquoise.

'Thank Heaven!' murmured the commander, dropping his glasses with a sigh of fervent relief.

The convoy had made its landfall.

II.

Some miles to the eastward, in a position almost directly ahead of the convoy, two officers dressed in the uniform of the Imperial German Navy stood upon the flattened summit of a tapered, cylindrical structure standing up out of the water for all the world like an innocent fairway buoy. But it was no buoy; it was the conning-tower of a submarine, and six feet beneath the surface, clearly visible through the green translucence of the water, was the huge, cigar-shaped hull of their vessel.

Through the open hatch beside them came the buzz of conversation from the interior, and the occasional hiss and chatter of a motor-pump, as, with a small reserve of buoyancy, the craft lay with her conning-tower just awash, ready for an instant dive. In less than thirty seconds a twirl of her propellers could have taken her out of sight on a long, downward slant.

To the north, distant perhaps eight miles, lay the line of the rugged coast, its hills, its valleys, and its woods and fields showing purple, brown, deep green, and golden in the strong sun. Farther to the east several delicate feathers of smoke rising almost vertically into the air told of the presence of a cluster of auxiliary patrol-vessels, which the submarine had passed earlier in the morning.

But it was neither at these nor at the land that the officers were gazing so intently. They did not seem to apprehend danger, and all their attention was concentrated on the western horizon, where a heavier smear of smoke stretching athwart the clear sky, and a forest of masts and funnels from a number of ships, as yet hull down, foretold the arrival of a convoy.

The *kapitän-leutnant*,* a small, sallow-faced little man with a morose expression and anxious eyes, put down his glasses.

'I can count seventeen,' he said gruffly. 'Some of them are large.'

'Any escort?' queried his subordinate, a tall, dapper-looking man with a rosy, youthful face, the black-and-white ribbon of the Iron Cross conspicuous at his button-hole, and a single gold stripe on his coat-sleeves.

'I cannot see them at present,' the captain answered, 'but I expect they will have the usual destroyers, and some armed trawlers if the convoy is slow.'

He spoke nervously, almost as if he were afraid.

'They are late, are they not?' asked the younger man.

The *kapitän-leutnant* nodded. 'Yes,' he

---

* In the German Navy a *kapitän-leutnant* corresponds to our lieutenant-commander, an *ober-leutnant* to our lieutenant, and a *leutnant* to our sub-lieutenant.

agreed. 'Our orders said they were due to pass this place at dawn.'

'It is unusual for this position to be so clear,' said the junior officer, glancing round the horizon and then overhead, as if he half-expected to see something. 'Generally we have sighted their coastal airships and sea-planes patrolling with destroyers and armed outpost boats, but to-day—nothing. Do you remember a month ago, somewhere near here, when we also saw nothing, but one of their submarines fired at us while we lay on the surface, and the torpedo passed directly underneath? We dived so deep that the rivets started to weep, and the '——

'No need to tell me the story,' snapped the captain, to whom the recollection was evidently unsavoury. 'I do not need you to help my memory!'

Von Hagen, the junior officer, smiled, and, unseen by his superior, shrugged his shoulders with easy tolerance.

'I was wondering,' he said, 'whether we were not a little too close to the land to be lying on the surface. It is a very clear day, and somebody ashore with good glasses might '——

'Pouf!' the captain snorted testily. 'Our conning-tower is not so conspicuous as all that. Anyhow, these fools of English would not know what it was, even if they saw it. They would think it was a buoy.'

'Fools they may be,' Von Hagen agreed; 'but there are no buoys here.'

'Do not argue with me!' growled the

commanding officer, with rapidly rising temper.
' When I require your advice I will ask for it.'

Von Hagen and Franck, the *kapitän-leutnant*
in command, lived a perpetual cat-and-dog
existence. They were always at loggerheads,
and hardly a day passed without bickering or
disagreement. In tastes and temperament, as
well as in appearance, the two men were the
direct antithesis of each other. They had
little in common; for Von Hagen, a regular
naval officer of noble birth, was something
of a dandy, and of a gay and pleasure-loving
disposition. Being high-spirited, he was certainly rather rash and venturesome at times;
but he was intelligent, almost clever. He
belonged essentially to the officer caste, and
therefore had a supreme contempt for those
of inferior station. Besides, he had only
lately come from a battleship to serve a short
apprenticeship as second in command before
being given charge of a submarine of his own.

Franck, on the other hand, though excitable,
was surly and discontented by disposition, a
natural boor. He had not been brought up
in the strict school of the Imperial Navy, and,
as an ex-officer of the reserve, would still have
been in the merchant service but for the war.
He knew nothing of the niceties and the
etiquette of the navy, and had all the distrust
and the dislike of his class for the pampered
aristocracy of which Von Hagen was a member.
Franck had been pitchforked into the submarine service at a time when, owing to
severe losses, volunteers were badly wanted,

and he had subsequently risen to command more by age and seniority than by ability or merit. His seniors, moreover, had come to look upon him with anything but a favourable eye, for he was slow and dull-witted, a man who, though he could be trusted to carry out orders, missed many opportunities through lack of initiative. He was a good seaman, perhaps, but a dismal failure as commander of a submarine, where technical knowledge is necessary.

He knew his own limitations, and cordially detested Von Hagen, with his airs of superiority, his immaculate dress, and his well-bred manner of speech and behaviour. He regarded him as an interloper who had been sent to spy out his actions, and to report thereon to higher authorities; for, some time since, Franck had been plainly given to understand that further failures and unsuccessful cruises would entail his being relieved of his command.

Von Hagen, though he realised that his captain hated him, was not there to note his deficiencies, and was not aware that even now he was ear-marked for the command of this self-same U-boat on Franck's contemplated supersession in the near future. But he did know that the man jarred upon him, and that his captain was ignorant, and unfitted for the position he held, for his incompetence was apparent even to the humblest member of the crew. He realised, also, that, for all his brusque and blustering manner, Franck was

really a weak man, and very timid at heart.
Sometimes, like other weak men, he was as
obstinate and as thick-headed as any mule;
but on occasions when things really mattered,
he often turned to his subordinate for advice,
acted upon it, and then took the credit to
himself.

So, while Von Hagen despised and distrusted
Franck, looked upon him with amused contempt and feelings of disgust, Franck, for his
part, was rather frightened of Von Hagen.
But, at the same time, he was cunning enough
to realise that his subordinate's ability often
stood him in good stead, and frequently saved
him from official odium and possible disgrace,
so he was anxious not to lose his services.

The German, unlike the Briton, is not a
seaman by instinct, and it is as easy to mingle
fire and water as to make a regular officer
of the Imperial Navy, imbued with the
arrogant spirit of Junkerdom, live in peace
and harmony with an ex-member of the
merchant service drawn from the ranks of
commerce or industry. They will work
together after a fashion, but not even the
common cause in war will quite obliterate
the instinctive feelings of class antagonism
and jealousy.

Von Hagen, rebuffed as usual, adroitly
changed the subject. 'When do you propose
to submerge?' he asked politely.

'When they are within ten miles. I want
to make certain of their course before having
to use the periscope.'

Von Hagen's face fell, for to him the proposal seemed to be suicidal. 'Ten miles!' he said, pursing his lips. 'It is a very clear day, and at that distance a good look-out could almost see our conning-tower. Do you not think it wise to'——

Franck turned upon him with a face of rage. 'You dare again to question my orders and to offer me advice!' he burst out passionately. 'Have I not said that I shall dive when they are ten miles off?'

'You have,' Von Hagen nodded, controlling himself with difficulty. 'But if I were in command'——

The remark was unfortunate, as a red rag to a bull.

'You are not in command!' thundered the captain, beside himself with anger. 'You are not in command—not yet! And until you are, it is I who will give the orders in this ship. Understand that!'

'Very well,' said Von Hagen resignedly. 'The responsibility is yours. I, as you say, am not in command.'

He saluted and turned to go below, for further conversation could only end in active strife. How he hated Franck!

But as he reached the foot of the conning-tower ladder and started to move forward, he was accosted by a wireless rating.

'There are signals coming through in code, *Herr Leutnant*,' the man said with a salute. 'They are being answered.'

'Tell the captain,' said Von Hagen.—

'Hartmann,' he added, turning to a petty officer, 'have the listeners at the hydrophones heard anything lately?'

'Nothing, *Herr Leutnant*,' the man replied, with a salute.

'Well, tell them to listen attentively. We may expect to hear—er—something at any time.'

And Von Hagen, though wireless meant nothing—for they heard it every hour of the day and night—experienced a vague feeling of uneasiness as he walked forward to his quarters.

III.

In an office ashore, whose plain, distempered walls were hung with charts and diagrams, a serious-faced man in the uniform of a captain of the Royal Navy sat at a desk stirring a cup of cocoa. He was idle for the moment, but in one corner of the room a deep-seated arm-chair, with a dented cushion and a rug flung carelessly across it, showed where he had spent the night. Moreover, the small table beside the chair, with its portable telephone, its well-filled ash-tray, half-smoked pipe, and a scribbled-over signal-pad, made it quite obvious that not all the night had been spent in slumber.

The windows faced east, and already the sun, shining out of a cloudless sky, bathed the room in a flood of brilliance. In a bare patch on the grassy slope outside two sparrows, twittering volubly, indulged in their morning dust-bath. Beyond, the hill fell steeply away

towards the harbour, until the gray slate roofs
of the water-side houses, with the blue smoke
curling lazily from their stubby chimneys,
seemed to be sitting, squat and stolid, on a
bed of green.

Over the roofs lay a wide expanse of
shimmering water, surrounded by hills. It
was the outer harbour, and terminated some
distance away in twin-headlands sharply
silhouetted against the pale blue of the sky.
Nearer at hand a bunch of rusty-looking
trawlers and a couple of gray destroyers lay
peacefully at buoys under the lee of a small,
rocky islet crowned with a gray stone fort.
Farther to the right, over the gently rising
ground, a number of slender masts and a thin
trickle of smoke against a background of
wooded hills betokened the presence of still
more ships.

A division of mine-sweeping trawlers in line
ahead, whooping stridently on their whistles,
bustled into view, and swung round the island
on their way towards the open sea. One of
the destroyers, raising steam, started to emit
clouds of inky-black smoke; and presently,
when knots of figures had appeared on deck,
she slipped from her buoy and scuttled fussily
seaward, with her white wake trailing out
astern.

The captain, noticing the sparrows, smiled
to himself, and started to crumble a biscuit.
He loved birds, and the two outside, since
they were creatures of habit, came there every
morning for their wash and brush up, in the

expectation of a subsequent breakfast. And
every third morning, when the captain had
had the 'night on,' they, together with
numerous friends and relations, were religi-
ously fed.

Rising from his chair, the officer pushed
the window noiselessly open and flung the
powdered remains outside. His guests instantly ceased their ablutions, and, shaking
the dust from their feathers, tentatively
regarded the meal before them with bright,
beady eyes. Then, summoning up courage,
they hopped forward and began their feast
within six feet of where the man stood
regarding them.

Presently half-a-dozen more sparrows appeared from the ivy overhead, and joined the
others with every symptom of delight; next,
a bedraggled robin, who, in the intervals of
nearly choking himself with the largest crumbs
he could find, spent his time in chivying the
commoner fry with angry chirrups; then a
young speckled thrush, four more sparrows,
and a starling.

'I'm evidently getting popular.' The captain smiled to himself, watching the throng of
birds intently, and reaching quietly for another
biscuit. 'I haven't seen that thrush before.
. . . Oh, dammit!' The telephone-bell had
suddenly wakened into activity with a whir
and a jangle which scattered the little flock,
with shrill cries of protest.

'Hallo!' he said, moving across to the table
and putting the receiver to his ear. 'Private

wire. Yes.—Who's that speaking?—Oh yes,
Commander Morton. Good-mornin', Morton.
—What?—Yes, I've got that. Where d'you
say she was sighted? — Ten miles! Silly
devils!—Yes, coast-watchers. I understand.
Good work—very.—You've informed everybody concerned, and Captain (D)* is taking
the necessary steps.—Yes.—Good. You want
me to tell the admiral and to warn the convoy.—No; a slow one this time, expecting to
get in sometime this afternoon.—M' yes, that
ought to do it, I should think. You can't be
too certain, though.—What? Is she the same
one?—Hold the line a moment. I'll have a
look.'

He left the instrument and stepped across
to a chart pinned to the wall. The surface
representing sea was pock-marked all over with
little red and yellow paper discs, bearing dates
and numbers. They showed the submarine
activity, the red representing actual sinkings,
and the yellow, abortive attacks. In the area
at which the captain was looking discs of both
colours were clustered very thickly indeed;
while here and there a green paper flag on a
pin, with a date and time marked in pencil,
showed where U-boats had actually been
seen and reported. He measured off a lati-
tude and longitude, stuck in a fresh green
flag, and measured the distance between it
and another.

'I thought so,' he murmured to himself,

* Captain (D)—that is, the captain in command of a destroyer
flotilla.

going back to the telephone. 'Working to the west'ard the whole time.'

'Morton,' he went on, speaking hurriedly into the instrument. 'Yes. She may be the same one.—Yes, possibly the boat that sank the *Albury* the day before yesterday. The patrols attacked her, you remember, and oil came to the surface, but there was no other result. Same boat, I expect, working to the west'ard towards the convoys.—Yes, that's it. —Hope we get her this time?—Yes, of course. —Humph!'—with a laugh—'I don't know so much about that. They're not fools.— Right-o! Good-bye!'

He hooked up the receiver and went across to the writing-table, where he pressed a bell-push and rapidly scribbled something on a slip of paper, marking it 'Urgent' in red chalk.

'Take this to the coding-office,' he said, rising from his chair and holding out a sealed envelope as the door opened and a marine orderly appeared. 'Don't waste any time, Riley.'

The marine saluted and departed on his errand, while the captain left the room to seek the admiral.

The door slammed, and presently the birds, regaining courage, returned one by one to their interrupted breakfast. Indeed, when the captain came back a few minutes later their numbers had visibly increased.

'Good business!' he said, breaking up the second biscuit. 'I'm blowed if that isn't a blackbird! First one I've seen this year.'

The captain was thinking of blackbirds, but just as he flung the powdery remains out of the window, a German submarine, a full eighty miles to the westward, disappeared beneath the surface. She lay directly in the track of an approaching convoy, and even now her captain was congratulating himself on the opportunity which was coming his way.

Faint wireless signals came in from the eastward, and were answered from quite close at hand. But the submarine, having dived, was deaf, and did not hear them.

IV.

It was an American destroyer far away on the port wing of the convoy who first saw the torpedo approaching. There had been no flutter of a periscope, no tell-tale splash in the water, as the weapon left its tube; merely that hard, whitened track of bubbles stretching straight across the clear bluish-green of the sea like a sun-baked footpath through a grassy meadow.

The convoy, having received the warning, had altered course clear of the danger area, and was well away to the southward, zig-zagging as it went. The destroyer was the only ship in the immediate neighbourhood, and hence it followed that the torpedo was fired at her.

Fritz, balked of his larger prey, and considering it inadvisable to come to the surface—as, indeed, it was—had remained below, where he could only travel at slow speed, and had evidently made up his mind to have a shot at anything that came his way. A small and handy vessel like a destroyer travelling at something over twenty knots is not an ideal target; it is a target, rather, which, since it is apt to retaliate in a sudden and nerve-racking manner, the greater number of German submarines do well to leave alone. But this particular U-boat, though not new to the game, was not very wise, and, disappointed of the larger fry, deliberately tempted Providence and fired. As luck would have it, the torpedo ran very straight.

It did not take the lieutenant-commander on the destroyer's bridge very long to make up his mind. He heard the shout of the gesticulating man on the forecastle, and saw the track lengthening out straight towards his port bow all in the same moment, and in an instant, with his heart in his mouth, he had rapped out the order,* 'Hard left!' to the helmsman.

The destroyer seemed to hang sluggishly before answering her helm, and already the end of that line of bubbles was within sixty

* It seems hardly necessary to point out that in the British Navy the order 'Hard a-starboard!' means that the steering-wheel is moved to the left, and that the ship's head travels round in the same direction. With 'Hard a-port!' the opposite takes place. The orders, in fact, refer to the direction in which the tiller moves—that is, in the opposite direction to the wheel and the ship's head, and are a survival of the old days when ships were steered with tillers.

In the United States Navy 'Hard left!' is the same as our 'Hard a-starboard!'—that is, the wheel and the ship's head both move to the *left*. 'Hard right!' similarly, corresponds to our 'Hard a-port!'

yards of the ship and heading straight for her.
The lieutenant-commander gazed anxiously at
it, for the torpedo itself must be some distance
ahead of its track, and never since the ship
had commissioned had she seemed so slow on
her helm.

Would she never start to turn?

Then, listing heavily until the water came
slopping over her low stern, she suddenly
began to swing, faster and faster. It was just
in time, for, even as she shot round, the track
flashed down her port side, merged into the
troubled water in her wake, and passed out
into the clear sea beyond. Whether the torpedo was running deep and went underneath
the ship, or whether it missed close astern,
nobody troubled to find out. A miss is as
good as a mile, anyway, and the lieutenant-
commander breathed again.

'Gee!' he exclaimed, motioning to the man
at the wheel to right his helm. 'Thought the
durned thing had us!'

'We're ready, cap'en,' said an excited ensign
close beside him. 'You just say the word
when I'm to start. You're running up the
track, I presume?'

'Yep,' the commanding officer nodded,
shading his eyes without looking round. 'A
shade more left, Pete. . . . Steady so, boy!'

The destroyer was travelling straight now,
straight as an arrow up that scarcely visible
track in the water. It got fainter and fainter
as she advanced. Then, 'Let go, one!' said
the lieutenant-commander. The ensign pulled

hard at a handle arrangement on the deck of the bridge and howled an unintelligible remark down a voice-pipe. Something heavy slid off the stern and fell into the water with a splash. 'Let go, two! Let go, three! Let go, four!'

Again the helm went over and the ship slithered round on her heel; but before she had completed a quarter-circle there came the deep, resounding thump of a heavy under-water explosion at the spot in her track where the first depth-charge had been dropped over-board.

A rounded hummock of whitish-gray water rose to the surface, and burst like a bubble in a fan of feathery spray.

Another explosion, with the same result. Another; and yet a fourth.

'Gee!' murmured the lieutenant-commander delightedly. 'I guess these British contraptions are some go!'

Then the unforgettable thing happened.

The rounded, gray bow of a large submarine suddenly broke surface within a hundred yards of the ship, and hung there with the water pouring off it. She seemed to be making efforts to rise, for the bows still travelled through the water, and, even as they watched, the top of her conning-tower appeared above the surface.

The destroyer was still steaming at full speed and turning rapidly, and the lieutenant-commander's first natural instinct was to adopt the speediest and surest method of sinking his enemy—that is, by ramming. But another look told him she was inside his turning circle. He could never bring about the desired collision unless he were to haul off and make a fresh start, by which time the submarine, if she were only temporarily disabled, might have dived out of harm's way.

Instead of that, he shouted to the men clustered round the foremost gun to open fire, and jumping at the port engine-room telegraph, wrenched it round to 'Stop,' and thence to 'Full astern,' to bring the ship round on her heel. And just as the reply-gongs clanged in answer the gun on the forecastle went off with a crash.

The shell struck short of the submarine's bow and ricochetted off into the distance with a whine, turning over and over in its flight, all the time clearly visible to the naked eye.

'Durn those fellows!' muttered the captain, as the port propeller started to go astern and the ship began to swing her bows towards the enemy. 'Why in hell can't'——

'Boomp!' went the weapon again; and this time the gun-pointer,* having overcome his pardonable excitement, aimed true, and sent the shell crashing into that gray bow.

A neat round hole suddenly appeared in the steel plating. Next, the thump of an explosion as the projectile burst inside, a little upheaval of splinters and débris, and a thin trickle of oily black smoke.

'Shoot at the conning-tower, boy! At the

---

* A 'gun-pointer' in the American Navy corresponds to our 'gun-layer.'

conning - tower !' the lieutenant - commander shouted, half-beside himself with anxiety lest his enemy should escape at the eleventh hour.

Even as he spoke the gun roared out again, the shell pitching into the sea some distance over its target. But before another round could be fired the conning-tower lid suddenly flew open and a man's head and shoulders appeared. He clambered out on to the super-structure, and waved his hands above his head, shouting something unintelligible at the top of his voice. He was followed by five other men dressed as seamen, and the whole party raised their arms and cried aloud for mercy. There was something abject and miserable about them. They were in evident terror of their lives, fearful lest they should be slaughtered.

'Hell !' muttered the gun-pointer disgust-edly, removing his eye from the telescopic sight. 'The durned scum ! Drowning inno-cent women and children one moment, and screeching to us to save their lives the next !'

No man, who is a man, can fire upon an enemy who has surrendered and is crying for mercy, and the gun-pointer, disappointed at being unable to finish the business with another shell, sauntered to the ship's side and evinced his displeasure by expectorating with some vehemence into the sea.

The bows of the stricken vessel reared them-selves in the air, and the conning-tower and superstructure dipped under, flinging its five occupants into the sea. For a moment the bows remained suspended in mid-air, until,

with a swift, gliding rush, they disappeared
for ever, and the onlookers found themselves
gazing at an area of seething, bubbling water
dotted with the heads of swimmers. Three
more men shot to the surface like corks after
she had disappeared—another rush of huge
bubbles breaking on the surface, and trails of
oil gradually spreading into an iridescent film
on the water.

It was all over. Nine survivors were
rescued; the rest were drowned outright, or
entombed in their steel prison fathoms below.

.   .   .   .   .   .

'Lord! listen to that cheering!' laughed
the senior officer of escorts a quarter of an
hour later, as the destroyer came scuttling
back to her station with the convoy, and passed
close under the stern of a transport crowded
with khaki-clad American troops. 'Can't
those "Sammies" yell? Does one good to
hear 'em.—Signalman! Make her a signal:
"Well done. Congratulate you most heartily
on your success. I guess you got right there."'

The reply was characteristic. 'We are
proud to have had the opportunity,' it said.
'Blood is thicker than water.'

'Blood is thicker than water,' murmured
the British officer, remembering where the
words were first used in this connection.* 'I

* I write subject to correction, but I think it was at the taking
of the Taku Forts during the war in China in the 'sixties that
Commodore Tatnall of the United States Navy, a strict but very
'benevolent' neutral, showed his neutrality by towing a British
vessel or some boats into action, with the remark, 'Blood is
thicker than water.'

should jolly well think it is; but I'll tell you one thing, sub.,' he added, turning to the young officer beside him.

'And what's that, sir?' asked the boy.

'When once these Yanks get going there's no stopping 'em,' the commander replied. 'Just think of what they're doing in France; think of what they're doing—er—everywhere! Splendid fellows! Keen as mustard! As for the skipper of that destroyer, I could fall on his neck and kiss him like a long-lost sister— some one else's sister, for preference!'

But the American lieutenant-commander was spared that final indignity.

CHAPTER XIII.

23RD APRIL 1918.

The game is more than the player of the game,
And the ship is more than the crew.
                        RUDYARD KIPLING.

I.

DURING the afternoon of 22nd April 1918, the eve of St George's Day, an observer standing on the wind-swept summit of the cliffs by the North Foreland lighthouse might have noticed an unusual concourse of vessels some distance out at sea. The area, even in war, is ever a busy one with the passage of mercantile traffic in and out of the Downs and the Thames estuary; but on this particular afternoon something out of the ordinary was evidently afoot. He would have seen the obsolete cruiser *Vindictive*, conspicuous by reason of her three lean funnels and the absence of masts save for a stump of foremast crowned with its circular fighting-top; the *Thetis*, the *Intrepid*, and the *Iphigenia*; the *Brilliant* and the *Sirius*, all small cruisers completed for sea in the 'nineties, vessels which had shown the White Ensign of Britain all over the world, but were now destined to end their days gloriously under the very muzzles of the enemy's guns. Old ships every one of them—ships that were long past their best days and could serve no useful purpose with a modern fleet. Nothing

L.S.   U

as a rule is more pathetic than a superannuated man-of-war, but the names of these vessels, together with those of the gallant souls who manned them, will pass down to posterity, and even now are written in letters of gold in the annals of the Royal Navy.

There were many more craft present—the *Iris* and the *Daffodil*, single-funnelled, stubby-looking little ferry-boats from the Mersey; a couple of old submarines; the ubiquitous destroyers; and a swarm of coastal motor-boats and motor-launches. And farther afield, at Dover and at Dunkirk, other forces were under steam in readiness—monitors and more destroyers, motor-launches and coastal motor-boats, both British and French—all to take part in the great adventure, the enterprise compared with which the risks of ordinary naval warfare fade into insignificance.

It was no haphazard operation, designed on the spur of the moment. Zeebrugge and Ostend, both used as submarine and destroyer bases by the enemy, had long proved thorns in our side, and in November 1917, in the absence of any more certain method, plans were first set on foot for the blocking of the two Flanders ports.

The mole at Zeebrugge consists of a long, curved breakwater of solid concrete jutting out into the sea, and affording the necessary protection to the twin-piers guarding the entrance to the inner basins and the Bruges Canal. At the shore end of the mole is a lattice-work viaduct which allows for the free flow of the tide, and without which the harbour could not have been prevented from silting up. The mole itself is about a mile long and eighty yards wide, and, like the foreshore bordering the entrance to the canal, was known to be studded with guns of all sizes and searchlights.

It was a foregone conclusion that the actual blocking-ships could never hope to get into the harbour unless the attention of the enemy were to be diverted by other means; and some time before they were due to arrive at their destinations, both Zeebrugge and Ostend were to be heavily bombarded by monitors at sea, by our shore batteries in the neighbourhood of Nieuport, and bombed by aircraft. Then, at the right moment, the *Vindictive*, the *Daffodil*, and the *Iris*, advancing in a smoke-screen to shield them from the enemy's view, were to dash alongside the Zeebrugge mole, land their storming-parties, capture the mole batteries, prevent the guns from firing on the blockships when they came in, and generally distract attention. At much the same time two old submarines filled with explosives were to make for the viaduct connecting the mole with the land, and, having wedged themselves in under the lattice-work, were to blow themselves up, destroy the viaduct, and make it impossible for any reinforcements to pass on to the mole proper. When this and the *Vindictive's* task had been effected, the *Thetis*, the *Intrepid*, and the *Iphigenia*, under the cover of another artificial fog, were to steam in and sink themselves in the canal entrance, their crews, together with those of the submarines, being taken off by motor-craft specially detailed for the purpose.

A very similar scheme was to be carried out at Ostend, except that, as there was no protecting mole at this place, the storming-parties and the submarines were not required.

Critics, had they known of the project, might well have held up their hands in horror. They could have drawn attention to Hobson's gallant but futile effort in the *Merrimac* to block the entrance to Santiago Harbour, and the desperate and repeated efforts of the Japanese to bottle the Russian fleet in Port Arthur. All these exploits ended in failure. And how could we, in the face of far greater difficulties, ever hope to seal Zeebrugge and Ostend ?

The blockships, remember, had to be taken through mined waters before reaching their objectives, through areas in which hostile destroyers would almost certainly be patrolling. And this having been achieved unseen, they, with over fifty attendant craft in the shape of destroyers, motor-launches, and fast motor-boats, were to be run into the very jaws of harbours situated in a flat, unlighted coast well provided with searchlights, and studded with guns of every calibre from 15-inch downwards—weapons which could make accurate shooting at something over twenty miles.

Wind, weather, visibility, and the state of the tide had all to be taken into account.

The operation could never be successful with an off-shore breeze, which would roll the smoke-screen seaward, and so expose the attackers to view; while bad weather, with a resultant sea, would effectually stultify the operations of the smaller craft, and prevent the *Vindictive*, the *Daffodil*, and the *Iris* from getting their storming-parties ashore. The tide, also, was an important factor, for the water had to be at a certain height to permit the *Vindictive's* hinged brows, or gangways, to reach the mole; while there must be no thick fog, but, for preference, a slight haze. The conditions, indeed, had to be ideal. And how often do four important factors work in conjunction? Very rarely.

Did people in responsible positions ever really imagine that the armada would get within a mile of its destination without being sunk, let alone through the outer harbours and into the narrow bottle-necks of the inner basins themselves?

But in war, given the right men, nothing is impossible.

A full five months before the attempt was actually made the preparations began. Not only had voluminous orders and instructions to be drafted out for every unit taking part, but the ships themselves had to be specially prepared, and, what was far more important, suitable officers and men obtained. Precisely how volunteers were selected one cannot say; but it is said that not even they themselves were aware, until well on into the proceedings, exactly what 'hazardous service' they were being called upon to undertake. Not that there would have been any hanging back if they had. If the news of the intended operation had been published broadcast, and volunteers publicly called for from the entire British Navy, the situation would have been impossible—much the same as in Togo's small fleet before Port Arthur, where, when less than a hundred men were required to man the blockships, several thousands applied, many of them signing their applications in their own blood.

The task of selection had to be done privily, and men were chosen from the Grand Fleet, from the naval depots at Portsmouth, Chatham, and Devonport, and from that ubiquitous and very gallant corps, the Royal Marines, both artillery and light infantry. Australasia, Canada, South Africa, and many another oversea dominion were represented.

Once chosen, every officer and man had to be specially trained for the part he was to play. The storming-parties had to be drilled in every detail of the operation. Men using hand-grenades, bombs, explosives for demolition purposes, flammenwerfers, and other unfamiliar and diabolical contrivances, had to be accustomed to their use; and not only this, they had to rehearse and rehearse again the whole operation on a full-scale model of Zeebrugge mole marked out on the ground. Every detail had to be considered. Each article of equipment had to be thought of. It had to be borne in mind that certain members of the storming-parties were to be provided with goggles, and wire-nippers with insulated handles for cutting barbed wire, and were to wear rubber-soled gymnastic shoes for a surer foot-hold; and that each man was to have a large white patch on his back and his chest, so that friends would recognise each other in the dark.

The actual blockships had to be filled up with rubble and cement, provided with pro-tection for their bridges, and gutted of all valuable fittings. The *Vindictive* had to be supplied with special fenders for going along-side, fitted with ramps and hinged brows for disembarking her storming-parties in the shortest possible time, and a variety of guns, howitzers, mortars, and flammenwerfers. Even the little *Daffodil* and the *Iris* had to be adapted for their special rôle, while no incon-siderable number of motor-craft had to be supplied with special smoke-producing plant for the creation of the necessary fog.

It was no small undertaking, and it had all to be kept a dead secret, for once the enemy got wind of the intention, the operation was fore-doomed. But in spite of the multitude of men engaged in the work of preparation, and those who were to be participators in the great event, the secret was kept. Those who knew of it kept their mouths tight shut. The officers and men in the Grand Fleet were completely in the dark. As for the general public, the news of the exploit was to them as complete a surprise as the exploit itself was to the Germans.

Before the actual operation there were two abortive attempts, when, at the eleventh hour, the weather rendered the undertaking impossible. The delay was a bitter disappointment to all concerned, but the experience was invaluable. But at last, on the eve of St George's Day, they set out on their desperate enterprise. Some of them were going to almost certain death; many did die gloriously in the face of the enemy; but one and all proved to the world that the hardy spirit of their ancestors did not lie dormant in their hearts.

II.

The *Vindictive* was timed to reach her destination exactly at midnight, but some time before this the aerial attacks and bombardments of Zeebrugge and Ostend were already in progress. Before long the flotilla of motor-launches and coastal motor-boats went ahead in the darkness to lay the necessary floats for making the smoke-screen across the harbour entrance, and presently the deep throbbing of heavy gun-fire, with the unearthly brilliance of star-shell bursting in the sky to the south-westward, showed that they had been seen and were being fired upon by the shore batteries.

The breeze, which up to this time had been blowing in a direction favourable to the attack —that is, towards the land—now died away, and before many minutes had passed, light airs, steadily increasing in force, were stealing sea-ward. This meant that the smoke, drifting out to sea, would leave the attackers clear in view of the enemy when they emerged from the pall.

It was a misfortune—a serious misfortune; but they did not hesitate. They were already committed to the venture, wind or no wind, and at seven minutes to midnight the *Vin-dictive* ran into a bank of artificial fog so thick that it was impossible to see more than half the length of her forecastle. Three minutes later she had passed through it, and, emerging into the clearer darkness beyond, immediately sighted the lighthouse at the head of the mole a few hundred yards distant on her port bow. Captain Carpenter promptly increased to full speed and altered course to go alongside.

Owing to the shift in the wind, and the fact that the enemy had succeeded in sinking several of the smoke-floats by gun-fire, the ship was now in full view of the batteries ashore, and almost at once every enemy weapon which would bear opened fire. The *Vindictive* re-plied, and in an instant the night became hideous with the deep, thudding roll of the discharges, the whinnying screech of projec-tiles, and the nerve-shattering crash, roar, and jangle as they drove home and burst.

Ahead, the orange flashes of the guns danced in and out of the dark shadows of the buildings ashore in a constant sparkle of flame. Star-shell and 'flaming onions' soared cease-lessly skywards to bathe the scene in their dazzling greenish-white glare until it was almost as bright as daylight; while the white, finger-like beams of many searchlights, with wreathing eddies of smoke from the guns filtering fantastically through their rays, added to the illumination. Nearer at hand the water spouted and boiled as projectiles fell.

The *Vindictive* was advancing into the mouth of hell. The hostile guns were firing at point-blank range, so that they could hardly miss her; but she never wavered. She drove steadily on, as steadily as the Light Brigade on the blood-stained field of Balaclava.

In the brief five minutes during which the ship ran the gauntlet — between the times she emerged from the friendly smoke-screen and arrived alongside the mole—she was hit repeatedly. Captain Halahan, in charge of the bluejacket storming-party, was killed as he stood in readiness to lead his men on to the mole; while Lieutenant-Colonel Elliot, in command of the marines, together with his second in command, Major Cordner, shared the same fate. Many other men, clustered on deck with their weapons in readiness to leap ashore the moment the ship got alongside, were also struck down, killed or wounded; while several of the hinged brows were demolished. But the *Vindictive* moved on, her guns booming defiance as she advanced.

It must have been an uncanny moment for any Germans on the mole when first they saw the ship appearing out of the smoke-

The *Vindictive* was advancing into the mouth of hell.

PAGE 312.

curtain. Her ghostly gray shape, magnified out of all proportion by her proximity, wreathed in a reek of smoke from her guns and exploding shell, and sparkling with the wicked-looking flashes of her weapons and the redder gouts of flame from shell bursting, must have seemed something from another world, something ghastly and supernatural, as she drove remorselessly towards them. But they were not afforded much time to analyse their feelings, for at one minute past midnight, with her pom-poms and machine-guns sweeping the mole, her mortars lobbing bombs over the parapet, and her heavy guns and howitzers firing shell at the hostile batteries, the ship was alongside.

She rubbed the wall with scarcely a tremor, and orders were at once given to let go an anchor. The *Daffodil*, however, which was to push her larger sister bodily into the mole, had been left behind when the *Vindictive* increased speed, and for some minutes the position was very precarious. Orders were inaudible in the uproar of the guns, and owing to a strong tide alongside the mole, and a heavy swell causing the ship to roll, she could not get close enough to land her storming-parties. Whichever way she put her helm, to star-board, to port, or amidships, the brows in the centre portion of the ship could not be made to reach the wall, neither could the special anchors for making her fast be properly secured. It was a terrible time, and the awful three or four minutes which elapsed until the

Daffodil arrived must have seemed a veritable purgatory.

But at last the little passenger-tender from the Mersey put her bows into the side of the *Vindictive* and pushed her in, and two brows were dropped. All the others had been destroyed or temporarily disabled by shell-fire. The storming-parties, led by their officers, instantly started to scramble ashore as best they could.

How the men ever landed seems little short of a miracle. The ship was rolling heavily in the backwash, and at one moment the ends of the brows were crashing against the mole, while the next they were eight or more feet in the air. Bluejackets and marines, fully accoutred and wearing gas-masks and steel helmets, some with rifles and fixed bayonets, some with Lewis guns, some with bombs and explosives, others with portable flame-throwers and all manner of other contrivances, had to make their way up these steep, wildly swaying bridges at the peril of their lives. They were under close-range fire from many machine-guns ; shells were still dropping all round them and bursting overhead ; while a stumble or a false foothold might have sent any of them tumbling to a certain and horrible death in the thirty-foot chasm between the ship and the mole.

It was enough to appal the bravest man ; but again there was no wavering, and the survivors of the storming-parties, leaving many dead and wounded behind them, swept ashore with a rush.

The *Daffodil,* on board of which were the officers and men of the demolition-parties, was ordered by Captain Carpenter to continue pushing the *Vindictive* into the wall, and remained doing this the whole time the larger vessel was alongside. At first it was thought that the little ship's boilers would not develop a sufficient head of steam for this difficult task, but, thanks to the wonderful work of Mr Sutton, her artificer-engineer, who succeeded in maintaining one hundred and sixty pounds pressure to the square inch in boilers only intended for eighty, the task was successfully accomplished.

The *Iris,* which had on board some further storming-parties, went alongside the mole ahead of the *Vindictive* to land her contingent, but had the greatest difficulty in securing, as there was a heavy swell and her grapnels would not span the parapet. An officer, Lieutenant-Commander Bradford, gallantly swarmed up a violently swaying derrick in an effort to secure the ship, but was shot almost as soon as he appeared over the parapet, to fall between the wall and the ship's side. Lieutenant Hawkins also climbed up a ladder and sat astride the wall, trying to make the ship fast; but he too was killed. Landing the men in these conditions was impossible, and to save further useless sacrifice of valuable lives she left her position, went alongside the *Vindictive,* and landed a few of her men across that ship.

Whilst alongside the mole the *Vindictive's*

hull was comparatively immune from shell-
fire, but funnels, upper works, and ventilators
showed above the wall, and were struck
every few seconds. The fighting-top above
the bridge, in which were stationed marines
manning pom-poms and Lewis guns, sustained
direct hits from shell which, on bursting,
killed every man except two. But Sergeant
Finch of the Royal Marine Artillery, himself
badly wounded and streaming with blood,
continued to use his gun until the top was
finally wrecked. He now wears the coveted
Victoria Cross.

The crew of the 7.5-inch howitzer on the
forecastle were killed or wounded to a man,
but the weapon was instantly manned by a
fresh crew. They, too, were exterminated;
but, nothing daunted at the fate of their
predecessors, a third party manned the gun
and continued to fire. Many of the deeds performed on that awful night passed unnoticed
in the turmoil of battle, but the men, to
quote the opinion of their officers, behaved
magnificently.

The main-deck of the *Vindictive* was a
ghastly shambles crowded with stricken men.
Ever since about 11.50, when the ship first
came under fire, a ceaseless flow of casualties
had been going below, until the temporary
dressing-stations on the mess-deck and in
the sick-bay overflowed, and room had to be
found for the wounded in the wardroom, the
cabins, and any spare space available. Most
of the wounds were severe, some of the men

were on the threshold of death, but one and all were possessed by the same indomitable spirit.

' Have we won, sir ? ' they anxiously asked Captain Carpenter as he went round. ' Have we won ? '

There is something sublime in the spirit of self-abnegation which animated the men on that memorable night. All ideas of self seemed to vanish utterly. Many of the brave fellows who lay there gritting their teeth in agony knew that their hours were numbered, but the thoughts of every one of them centred on that all-important question — ' Have we won ? '

No written description can ever convey an adequate idea of the awful nature of the fighting on the mole itself; but, shelled by heavy guns, fired upon at close range by snipers and machine-guns, the storming and demolition parties did what they set out to do. The arrangement of the mole itself, with its batteries, its concrete shelters, its sheds, and its seaplane station, was more or less known beforehand; but studying its geography from plans and aeroplane photographs in peace and quietness, and storming the place at midnight under heavy fire and in the dazzling glare of searchlights and star-shell, are two very different things. There were pitfalls everywhere—railway-lines for heavily laden men to trip over, barbed-wire entanglements to catch them if they were unwary, sheer drops of a dozen feet on to the solid concrete below;

and through it all the unremitting swish and crackle of the machine-gun bullets, the roar, crash, and thunder of exploding shell.

Abreast of where the *Vindictive* lay was a German destroyer. She was heavily fired upon, and a few of her men scrambled on to the mole, instantly to be bayoneted or shot by the storming-parties. Other men pelted the destroyer with bombs and explosives, and there seemed little doubt that she was sunk.

Buildings, gun-emplacements, and bomb-proof shelters were attacked and bombed in turn; while several more isolated parties of the enemy were cut off and disposed of. Side by side with the bluejackets and the marines went a little party of air mechanics with portable flammenwerfers and phosphorus bombs. Their work was invaluable. But the casualties among the storming-parties were very severe, for, in addition to the heavy and accurate fire from the shore batteries and the machine-guns on the mole itself, the German destroyers alongside also joined in the battle.

And so the struggle on the mole continued, the men fighting shoulder to shoulder to storm the gun-positions; shooting, bayoneting, bombing in the glare and sulphurous smoke of the shell explosions; men dropping right and left, and the wounded crawling painfully back to the doubtful shelter of the *Vindictive*.

Meanwhile, from another direction, a gallant little band of six men was slowly approaching the viaduct at the shore end of the mole in an antiquated submarine, C3, filled with explosives. Their names—Lieutenants Sandford, of the Royal Navy, and Howell Price, of the Royal Naval Reserve; Petty Officer W. Harner; Engine-Room Artificer G. Roxburgh; Leading Seaman Maver; and Stoker H. C. Bindall—deserve to be remembered, for theirs was probably the most hazardous and nerve-testing task of that eventful night.

It had originally been intended to attack the viaduct with two submarines, but the second, due to a mishap which nobody could have avoided, was not able to reach her destination in time to take her share. Her officers and men were bitterly disappointed, and on their return immediately proffered their services for another attempt.

C 3 was provided with an automatic steering-device to enable her to maintain a steady course if the men abandoned her a few hundred yards from the viaduct, while a small skiff fitted with a motor provided the means for the crew to escape. But there was always the remote prospect that something might go wrong with the steering-gear at the last moment, and sooner than leave anything to chance, Lieutenant Sandford and his brave fellows determined not to abandon their craft until they had wedged her firmly in underneath the viaduct.

It was a heroic resolve. The viaduct, they well knew, would be crowded with the enemy, and there was every prospect that the motor-skiff would be shot to pieces by gun and rifle fire before ever they reached their destination. As an alternative method of escape they might possibly scramble ashore and make their way to the *Vindictive* along the mole; but if they were unable to effect this, they had every intention of lighting the fuse, and of perishing in the resulting explosion.

It was no desperate plan made on the spur of the moment in the heat of battle. It was premeditated, and these six volunteers were unanimous. Life was as dear to them as it is to other men, but they realised that their task was merely part and parcel of an operation, the success of which must not be jeopardised through their unwillingness to make the supreme sacrifice. Whatever happened, the viaduct must be blown up. They, if necessary, would go up with it.

While the submarine was still at a distance of over a mile from her objective she was lit up in the glare of a star-shell. At about the same time a few rounds were fired at her, but the enemy soon ceased his attentions, and by about midnight the mole and the viaduct, clearly silhouetted against the glare of flares burnt by the enemy, was within half a mile. The crew were mustered on deck in readiness for the final effort, and almost at once the boat was temporarily illuminated in the beams of two searchlights.

The hostile guns, however, refrained from firing. Possibly they were too busy with other targets, or else the enemy imagined that

the submarine was trying to get into the
harbour, had missed her way, and was blindly
blundering into collision with the mole, in
which condition they could make short work
of her, even capture her. They little guessed
her real errand. If they had, they would
have opened fire with every gun that would
bear.

A few minutes later she altered course
straight for the viaduct at full speed, a little
more than nine knots. The lattice-work itself,
true to their expectation, was crowded with
riflemen; but, imagining the craft to be running crazily to certain destruction, they did
not open fire.

Nearer and nearer came the viaduct. The
crash came, and C 3 struck under their very
noses. She took the structure exactly between
two uprights, and, lifting bodily into the air
as she rode over the horizontal girders, drove
on until the foreside of her conning-tower
crashed into the lattice-work. There she
brought up.

The motor-skiff was lowered at once, but as
she was dropped into the water the propeller
was hopelessly damaged against a projection.
The crew took their places in her and manned
the two oars, leaving Lieutenant Sandford
on board the submarine to light the fuses.
Having done this, he joined his men in the
boat; and, shoving off, they started to pull
away for their lives against the strong current.
They could hear orders shouted overhead,
could see Germans dropping down from the

viaduct on to the deck of the submarine. A moment later two searchlights blazed out, and the frail cockle-shell instantly became a target for every pom-pom, machine-gun, and rifle in the vicinity. They were shooting at point-blank range, and so great was the volume of fire that one man of the party states that the swish and plop of the bullets striking the boat and dropping into the water all round completely drowned the sounds of the firing.

The skiff was soon holed in many places, and it was only by dint of using a pump, which had luckily been provided as an after-thought, that they succeeded in keeping her afloat. Then Lieutenant Sandford was hit twice in rapid succession, followed almost immediately afterwards by the petty officer and the stoker. But the others still tugged at the oars, nerving every effort to get to a place of safety before the inevitable explosion took place. Their progress with only two oars in the teeth of the current was appallingly slow.

At last, at twenty minutes past mid-night, when the boat was still within three hundred yards of the viaduct, the charge detonated. There came the shattering roar of a huge explosion, and a blinding sheet of orange flame, mingled with pieces of wreckage from the submarine; and the viaduct itself shot skywards. An arch of liquid fire, caused by blazing petrol from the submarine's fuel-tanks, curved across the heavens, over the heads of the men in their boat, and fell sizzling and steaming into the water beyond. A shower of débris, mingled with fragments of solid masonry, and perhaps the mutilated bodies of Germans, came raining down into the sea all round them. . . .

The searchlights ashore suddenly vanished. The firing ceased, and in that brief instant the viaduct was utterly demolished, and many of the enemy went to their death. There came a few minutes' silence, followed by a roar of frenzied cheering from the *Vindictive's* storming-parties on the mole. Then the crackle of musketry and the roar and thunder of the heavier guns broke out afresh as the fight recommenced.

The men of C 3 had successfully accomplished their mission, and a few minutes later the gallant little party were picked up by a picket-boat specially detailed for the purpose, and commanded by Lieutenant-Commander Sandford, Lieutenant Sandford's brother, who took his boat in under the fire of the guns to effect the rescue. The picket-boat was holed in the process, but got away in safety, and, having transferred the wounded, eventually managed to return to Dover under her own steam.

III.

At twenty minutes past midnight the *Thetis*, the leading blockship, commanded by Commander Ralph S. Sneyd, D.S.O., steamed past the end of the mole. After her came the

Intrepid, Lieutenant Stuart Bonham-Carter, and the *Iphigenia*, Lieutenant Edward W. Billyard-Leake.

Theirs was the most important phase of the operation, for the storming of the mole by the *Vindictive's* men, and the blowing up and destruction of the viaduct by the submarine, were both subsidiary and contributory to the actual blocking of the harbour entrance.

Rockets fired from the *Vindictive* gave the *Intrepid* a chance of seeing her whereabouts, and rounding the lighthouse at the end of the mole, she steered straight for the entrance in the boom, a contrivance of nets and heavy wires strung out between barges. As she came in, her guns opened fire on the hostile batteries, she in turn being subjected to a tornado of fire from the guns ashore. She was hit repeatedly; and those who witnessed her entry say that her gray hull, wreathed in smoke, dim and ghostly against the brilliance of the searchlights beyond, sparkled wickedly with the flame of her own guns, and glowed redly with the bursts of exploding shell. It was a sight never to be forgotten.

The *Thetis* steamed on towards the opening between the barges, but as she was swinging fast and could not be checked in time, she had the misfortune to run into the net obstruction, which, being gathered into her propellers, soon brought them to a standstill. Carrying her way, she still forged ahead, taking the nets with her; but presently, practically unmanageable, she bumped on the bottom. She eventually slid off again into the deeper water of the dredged channel, but, having been frequently hit, was heeling over and settling down fast.

The piers at the canal entrance were actually in sight, but nothing further could be done; and signalling to the *Intrepid* and the *Iphigenia* to point out the clear passage, Commander Sneyd gave orders for his vessel to be abandoned. Waiting until the engine and boiler rooms were clear of men, he then pressed the firing-keys and blew her up. The ship began to sink fast, and her ship's company, many of them wounded or suffering from the effects of gas, manned the single cutter which was left to them, and rowed to their attendant motor-launch.

The *Thetis*, thanks to a series of circumstances which no power on earth could have guarded against, was therefore denied the supreme satisfaction of sinking herself exactly in the position laid down for her between the jetties leading to the inner harbour; but she was in the fairway outside, where she was scarcely less useful in blocking the exit. Moreover, her signals to her consorts played no small part in helping them to achieve complete success.

The second blockship, the *Intrepid*, commanded by Lieutenant Stuart Bonham-Carter, was following close on the heels of the *Thetis*, and, passing that ship as she lay sinking, steered straight for the mouth of the canal.

Owing to delay some time before in a motor-launch getting alongside to take off her spare crew, and due also, it is said, to the extreme reluctance on the part of the men themselves to miss the fight, she went in with her spare watch of stokers still on board, so that her ship's company, instead of fifty-four, numbered eighty-seven souls.

Most of the hostile guns were concentrating their fire on the *Vindictive*, the mole, and the *Thetis;* and passing between the piers, the *Intrepid* steamed on up the canal without much interference beyond shrapnel-fire. Having reached a position several hundred yards inside the line of the shore, Lieutenant Bonham-Carter put the bows of his ship in towards the western bank, and worked the propellers to swing the stern well across the canal. There, having given orders to abandon ship, he exploded the charges to sink her.

The greater number of the officers and men got away in boats, and were duly picked up; but the commanding officer himself, two other officers, and four petty officers were reduced to nothing better than a Carley float, a huge life-buoy arrangement expressly designed for carrying a large number of men. Launching this unwieldly contrivance, a calcium light attached to which burst into brilliant flame the moment it touched the water, they paddled slowly down the canal, with bullets from the machine-guns on the bank pattering into the water all round them. How this party ever

succeeded in making their escape is nothing
short of a miracle. They had nothing with
which to propel their lumbering float except
a few short paddles, and had it not been for
Lieutenant Percy T. Dean, R.N.V.R., of
Motor-Launch 282, who brought his little
ship into the canal on the heels of the *Intrepid*,
and rescued them under the withering fire of
the machine-guns, they could hardly have sur-
vived to tell the tale.

The *Iphigenia*, the third blockship, in command of Lieutenant E. W. Billyard-Leake,
arrived soon after the *Intrepid*. She also
came under fire as she passed through the
outer harbour, while a bursting shell severed
a steam-pipe and shrouded the forepart of the
vessel in clouds of steam. The smoke from
the *Intrepid*, moreover, was floating about the
canal entrance, and made it very difficult to
see; but driving in between a dredger and
a barge, and carrying the latter with her,
Lieutenant Billyard-Leake steamed his ship
on up the canal. He then manœuvred to
place the *Iphigenia* in the gap between the
Intrepid and the eastern bank, and after
ringing the alarm-gong for the ship to be
abandoned, exploded the charges.

The crew left the ship in one cutter, the
other being too badly damaged by shell-fire
to be of any use, and, peppered by bursting
shrapnel and pelted by machine-guns, they
pulled clear of the sinking ship. Motor-
Launch 282 was still in the vicinity, rescuing
the men of the *Intrepid*, and seeing her near

the bows of his own ship, Lieutenant Billyard-Leake went alongside and transferred most of his men. The others stayed in the cutter, which was made fast to the bow of the motor-launch, and the latter went full speed, stern first, down the canal.

It was realised from the very beginning that the crews of the blockships had a very slender chance of getting away with their lives. They had to sink their ships well inside the jaws of a narrow harbour fringed with machine-guns, and the approaches to which were commanded by guns of all sizes and illuminated by searchlights. Having abandoned their vessels, they then had to run the gauntlet in their boats; and had it not been for the magnificent work of Lieutenant Dean and his volunteer crew in their motor-launch, hardly one of them could have escaped.

A motor-launch is unarmoured. She has a wooden hull, which can be pierced by any bullet, and in ordinary circumstances is none too easy to handle. Yet, without the least regard for their own personal safety, the lieutenant and his men took their craft up the canal in face of the fire from the banks, hovered about picking men out of the water and from the boats of the blockships, and then retired with their little ship so crammed with the one hundred and fifty men aboard that she was in imminent danger of capsizing. To make matters worse, she suffered many casualties from the incessant fire of the machine-guns; while her steering-gear jammed on leaving the canal, necessitating the undesirable expedient of steering with the screws. Lieutenant Dean received the Victoria Cross for his gallantry, and never has the decoration been more richly deserved.

IV.

Included in the swarm of other vessels detailed to take part in the operation were numbers of coastal motor-boats, small, powerfully engined craft built on the hydroplane principle, and capable of a speed of something over thirty knots in calm water. For many months they had been used with conspicuous success off the Belgian coast, darting in at night close under the enemy's guns and searchlights to attack destroyers with their torpedoes, and for reconnaissance work generally. They were particularly suitable for this function on account of their light draught, great speed, and small size, which, besides permitting them to work in shoal water at all stages of the tide, made it extremely difficult for the German gunners to knock them out. It is one thing to put a shell into a large and slowly moving ship, but quite another proposition to hit a small object with nothing visible to aim at except two enormous feathers of water careering along in the darkness at the speed of an ordinary passenger-train.

These craft, as may well be imagined, were

officered and manned by young men who
gave no thought for the morrow. They were
used to hurtling about within point-blank
range of the guns, and on the night of
April 22–23 they again proved their value.
Some were detailed for making the necessary smoke-screens off the harbour entrance
—work which brought them their fair share
of attention from the batteries. Others
had the more exciting tasks of attacking the
mole with Stokes guns before the *Vindictive* got alongside, with the object of
making the German gunners take shelter
in their bomb-proofs, or of firing their torpedoes at vessels alongside the inner face
of the mole when once the blockships had
passed.

As an example of the spirit which animated
the personnel of these C.M.B.'s, and to show
their firm determination not to miss the fight,
there is the case of No. 35A, commanded by
Lieutenant Edward Hill. This boat sailed
from Dover with the others at about 3.30 on
the afternoon of April 22, but a few hours
later, when eighteen miles from her starting-
place, had the misfortune to foul her propellers.
Nothing could be done on the spot to clear
them, but at 6.30 a drifter arrived on the
scene, took the damaged craft in tow, and
arrived with her at Dover at 8 o'clock. She
was immediately hoisted out of the water,
when, besides fouled propellers, it was found
she had sustained other damage. This was
rectified, and at 9.40 she was once more in

the water, and set off at full speed for her rendezvous off the Belgian coast. She eventually arrived off Zeebrugge, a matter of some seventy miles, ten minutes before midnight, and proceeded to carry out her share in the smoke-screening operations as if nothing at all out of the ordinary had happened.

Most of the destroyers present were employed in covering the flotillas of motor-launches and motor-boats responsible for making the smoke-screens; and though the greater number of them came under fire at one time or another, it is not possible here to give details of their movements.

The *Warwick*, on board of which was Sir Roger Keyes himself, together with the *Phœbe* and the *North Star*, was stationed close inshore to attack any hostile destroyers leaving the harbour; and throughout the operation the *Warwick*, sometimes under heavy fire, remained within a few hundred yards of the *Vindictive* as she lay alongside the mole. But of all the destroyers present, the *North Star* and the *Phœbe* had the most thrilling experience.

The first-named, commanded by Lieutenant-Commander K. C. Helyar, lost touch in the thick smoke, and after casting round to find the *Vindictive* or her consorts, sighted land ahead shortly before one o'clock. Altering course again, she presently found herself actually inside the area enclosed by the curved mole, with the blockships in sight ahead, and

the mole itself, with several German destroyers
alongside it, to starboard. She was instantly
lit up by a searchlight, and firing a torpedo
at one of the hostile vessels, put her helm hard
over to escape from her unenviable position.
The ship swung rapidly, but while she slewed
towards the mole the batteries opened a furious
fire. Shell fell all round her, many driving
home; but, firing more torpedoes, she still
continued to turn. The lighthouse at the
extremity of the mole was sighted, and at first
it was touch-and-go whether or not she could
clear it. This she succeeded in doing, but, on
passing at little more than a hundred yards,
was struck by two successive salvos of shell
in the engine and boiler rooms. Engines and
boilers alike were rendered useless, and, with
her motive-power gone, the ship finally came
to rest within four hundred yards of the end
of the mole, a searchlight still blazing full
upon her, and shell crashing into her every
few seconds.

But help was forthcoming, for the *Phœbe*,
commanded by Lieutenant-Commander H. E.
Gore-Langton, which was outside, had observed
through a rift in the smoke the *North Star*
passing the mole-head on her way out, and
had seen her struck and brought to a standstill. He at once proceeded to her assistance,
and steaming between the injured vessel and
the mole, made a smoke-screen to shield her
from view. Having done this, he placed his
ship ahead of the *North Star* and passed a
wire across to tow her out of action. By the

time this was completed both ships had drifted some distance to the north-eastward, with the *North Star* lying approximately at right angles to the *Phœbe*. A shift in the wind, moreover, had dissipated the smoke-screen, and once more both vessels were lit up in the rays of searchlights and the glare of star-shell, and were being heavily fired upon at short range. Going slowly ahead, the *Phœbe* then tried to drag her damaged consort round to the desired course, but the *North Star*, badly battered, and with her engine and boiler-rooms flooded, lay water-logged, so that the towing-wire snapped like pack-thread as soon as the strain came upon it.

Lieutenant-Commander Gore-Langton then turned his ship and secured alongside the wreck with the intention of drawing her farther out before again attempting to tow from ahead. During this period both ships were once more fully illuminated, and several salvos of shell struck, cutting the securing wires, blowing the *North Star's* capstan overboard, and killing and wounding many men. Unable to carry out her intention, the *Phœbe* thereupon cast off, made another smoke-screen between the *North Star* and the shore, and, lying off, sent a boat to rescue the survivors. The *North Star* also lowered her boats and ferried some of her men across.

Both ships were still under accurate and heavy fire ; and, circling round again, Lieutenant-Commander Gore-Langton made a further smoke-screen to cover his movements, and then, for the third time, closed the wreck and went alongside. Again he attempted to tow her clear, but again the *North Star* was hit repeatedly; and seeing that she was sinking fast, and that further efforts would only result in the loss of both ships, he reluctantly gave orders for her to be abandoned. The men scrambled across, and the *Phœbe* backed astern, when it was noticed that one man had been left behind. The wreck was reapproached to effect his rescue, but as the *Phœbe* came alongside the man was killed by a bursting shell.

The port side of the *North Star* was riddled like a sieve, the water was gaining fast, and more shell were bursting on board every moment; and finally, seeing she was doomed, the *Phœbe* retired under heavy fire.

From first to last she had stood by her stricken friend for nearly an hour under the unremitting and accurate close-range fire of the batteries; and the rescue of the *North Star's* crew, which was effected in circumstances which might also have involved the loss of the *Phœbe*, was entirely due to the coolness and gallant conduct of Lieutenant-Commander Gore-Langton and his ship's company, behaviour in which the officers and men of the *North Star* were not one whit behind-hand. It has never been the custom in the British Navy to desert a comrade in distress, and on this occasion the old tradition was more than upheld.

V.

At about ten minutes to one, as the block-ships were in and the submarine had accomplished her purpose, Captain Carpenter, in the *Vindictive*, gave the necessary signal for the retirement of the storming-parties on the mole. A quarter of an hour later it was reported that no further officers or men were coming on board, and after another five minutes' grace, the *Daffodil* started to tow the *Vindictive's* bows away from the wall.

The *Iris*, which had shoved off some minutes previously, had come under very heavy fire on getting clear, and, crowded as she was with men, suffered very heavy casualties, including Commander Valentine Gibbs, who was mortally wounded by a shell which severed both legs, and Lieutenant Spencer, R.N.R., the navigating officer. Serious fires also broke out on board, due to shell igniting some ammunition; but, taking charge of the ship, the next officer, Lieutenant Oscar Henderson, took her seaward. Luckily the engines and boilers were intact; but her casualties were enormous—eight officers and sixty-nine men being killed, and three officers and a hundred and two men wounded.

Presently, blazing like a furnace, her flaming funnels torn and battered out of all recognition, and her upper deck a shambles of twisted steel, the *Vindictive* left the mole, circled round, and made for home. Captain

Carpenter had just been wounded, but steered the ship himself; and, followed by salvos of German shell which fell into the water all round her, the gallant old ship disappeared in the billowing clouds of smoke to seaward.

The *Sirius* and the *Brilliant*, the two block-ships detailed to seal the harbour entrance at Ostend, did not succeed in reaching their objective, owing to the removal of a buoy, and the off-shore wind blowing the smoke-screens seaward. They came into full view of the enemy's guns, were heavily pounded, and, having failed to find the entrance, grounded some distance to the eastward. It was nobody's fault. It was a mere vicissitude of war. Commander Godsal, who commanded the *Sirius* in the first endeavour, had charge of the *Vindictive* on the second and final attempt to seal the harbour. It was successful, but the gallant commander met his death after having placed his ship in the entrance.

When the sun rose on St George's Day, an antiquated cruiser, many destroyers, and numbers of motor-launches and coastal motor-boats might have been seen wending their way homeward towards their respective bases. They had left something tangible behind them, in the shape of two charred, shell-riven wrecks in the canal at Zeebrugge, and two more on the beach near Ostend. But something even more imperishable had risen out of those battered hulls. Ships may come and ships may go; men may rise to fame and pass away; but the memory of the gallant dead, those of that band of brothers who strove and fought for Britain on St George's Day, will surely never fade.

THE END.

Edinburgh:
Printed by W. & R. Chambers, Limited.

Edinburgh:
Printed by W. & R. Chambers, Limited.